Understanding Science 3

Joe Boyd
Assistant Head, St David's High School, Dalkeith
Walter Whitelaw
Assistant Science Adviser, Lothian
and
Peter Warren
Co-ordinator of Science, Acton High School, London

JOHN MURRAY

Advisory panel
Peter Leckstein: *Inspector for Living Science, London Borough of Wandsworth*
Lesley Campbell: *Health Education Adviser*
Terry Allsop: *Lecturer in Education Studies, Oxford University*

The authors would like to thank their wives and families for their support and tolerance throughout the project.

First published 1991
by John Murray (Publishers) Ltd
50 Albemarle Street, London W1X 4BD

Designed by Impress International, 33540 France
Typeset by Blackpool Typesetting Services Ltd, Blackpool
Printed by Mateu Cromo Artes Graficas, S.A., Madrid

British Library Cataloguing in Publication Data
Boyd, Joe
Understanding science 3
1. Science - for schools
I. Title II. Whitelaw, Walter III. Warren, Peter
500

ISBN 0-7195-4824-1 Pupils' book
ISBN 0-7195-4825-X Teachers' resource book

Contents

Extensions

This symbol indicates an extra research task for you to do on your own. Keep the information you gather in a special file.

Acknowledgements

CARTOONS: Ainslie MacLeod
COLOUR ARTWORK: Peter Bull, Linden Artists, Nancy Sutcliffe
LINE DRAWINGS: Art Construction, RDL Artset
COVER PHOTO: ZEFA

The following have provided photographs or given permission for copyright photographs or items to be reproduced:

p.8 *top left* Gerald Cubitt/Bruce Coleman Ltd; *top right* Peter Stevenson/Planet Earth Pictures; *centre left* Dr B. Booth/GSF Picture Library; *centre right* P. Thurston/ GSF Picture Library; *bottom left* ZEFA; *bottom right* David T. Grewcock/Frank Lane Picture Agency
p.12 *top and bottom* ZEFA; *centre* Steve Nicholls/Planet Earth Pictures
p.13 G. I. Bernard/NHPA
p.16 *top* A. R. Hamblin/Frank Lane Picture Agency; *bottom* Siegfried Kerscher/Frank Lane Picture Agency
p.26 Mark N. Boulton/Bruce Coleman Ltd
p.27 *left and right* Tony Langham
p.28 *left* Barnaby's Picture Library; *centre* Mike Wells/Aspect Picture Library; *right* Dr J. E. Jackson, East Malling Research Station
p.29 *a, c and f* ZEFA; *d* Kemira Fertilisers; *h* Suttons Seeds Ltd
p.31 *a* John Howard/Science Photo Library; *b* Alex Bartel/Science Photo Library; *c and d* ZEFA
p.35 *2* ZEFA; *3* Norman Tomalin/Bruce Coleman Ltd; *4, 5, 7 and 8* Tom Harrison
p.37 *a, b and d* Stephen Dalton/NHPA; *c* James Hudnall/Planet Earth Pictures
p.39 *top left* John Howard/Science Photo Library; *top right* ZEFA; *bottom left* Chris Gilbert; *bottom right* Department of Health
p.44 Dave Williams
p.51 *1* The Royal National Institute for the Deaf; *2* Akai (UK) Ltd; *3* Dave Williams; *4* Sound Advantage
p.52 *top* Nicéphore Niépce/Gernsheim Collection, Harry Ransom Humanities Research Center, The University of Texas at Austin; *top centre* Henry Fox Talbot/Hulton-Deutsch Collection, The Hulton Picture Company; *bottom centre* Louis Daguerre/Hulton-Deutsch Collection, The Hulton Picture Company; *bottom* Thomas Sutton/Trustees of the Science Museum
p.54 *top left* Peter Menzell/Science Photo Library; *top right* J. Wooldridge/GSF Picture Library; *bottom left* David E. Rowley/Planet Earth Pictures; *bottom right* Simon Fraser/Science Photo Library
p.55 *top left* Ivor Edmonds/Planet Earth Pictures; *top right* John Reader/Science Photo Library; *bottom left* Dinosaur National Monument/GSF Picture Library; *bottom right* ZEFA
p.56 *top* NASA/Science Photo Library; *centre* Fred Espenak/Science Photo Library; *bottom* Royal Observatory, Edinburgh; *inset bottom left* Kim Gordon/Science Photo Library; *inset bottom right* NASA/Science Photo Library
p.59 *far left and left* John Lythgoe/Planet Earth Pictures; *right* Jack Finch/Science Photo Library; *far right* John Sanford/Science Photo Library
p.60 *a, b, d, f and h* Dr B. Booth/GSF Picture Library; *c* Adrian Davies/Bruce Coleman Ltd;
e John Wilson/Science Photo Library; *g* ZEFA
p.63 *top far left* Astrid & Hans-Frieder Michler/Science Photo Library; *top left, top far right and bottom far right* ZEFA; *top right and bottom right* Dr B. Booth/GSF Picture Library; *bottom far left* Charlie Ott/Bruce Coleman Ltd; *bottom left* Alf Powell/BICC
p.64 NASA/Associated Press
p.65 *a left* N. A. Callow/NHPA; *a right* M. I. Wacker/NHPA; *b* Dr B. Booth/GSF Picture Library; *c* Michael Marten/Science Photo Library; *d* J. G. James/Planet Earth Pictures;
e James Carmichael/NHPA
p.61 *top* Kim Gordon/Science Photo Library; *bottom* Bruce Coleman Ltd
p.71 *left and centre* ZEFA; *right* David Purdie
p.83 *top left* ZEFA; *top centre* Flip Schulke (NASA)/Planet Earth Pictures; *top right* Anthony Bannister/NHPA; *bottom* Silvestris/Frank Lane Picture Agency
p.84 *top and bottom* Mary Evans Picture Library
p.90 *top* Sally Morgan/Ecoscene; *bottom* David Purdie
p.94 *left* Kemira Fertilisers; *right* ICI Katalco
p.95 Chemical Design Ltd/Science Photo Library
p.96 Dr B. Booth/GSF Picture Library
p.99 *all photos* Dr B. Booth/GSF Picture Library
p.101 *top* AEA Technology; *bottom left and right* ZEFA
p.110 Dave Williams
p.118 British Telecom
p.121 *top left* Geoff du Feu/Planet Earth Pictures; *top right and bottom left* ZEFA; *bottom right* David Purdie
p.122 *top* Michael Freeman/Bruce Coleman Ltd; *centre* Dr B. Booth/GSF Picture Library; *bottom* Cem-FIL International Limited
p.126 *both photos* © Crown copyright/Fire Research Station
p.128 *left and centre* Quadrant/Colourviws ICM; *right* David Woodfall/NHPA
p.129 *left* English Heritage; *right* David Purdie
p.130 *far left* P G Products Ltd; *left* Dr B. Booth/GSF Picture Library; *upper right* ZEFA; *lower right* Paint Research Association; *far right* W. David and Sons Limited
p.133 *parts 1, 2 and 4* adapted from *BP Statistical Review of World Energy July 1989*/British Petroleum Company PLC
p.134 *top left* Dr B. Booth/GSF Picture Library; *top right* (brooch by Jane Adam) Jane Adam/Craft Council; *centre* Ken Lucas/Planet Earth Pictures; *bottom left* W. Canning Materials Ltd; *bottom centre and right* Jane Burton/Bruce Coleman Ltd
p.137 Stephen Dalton/NHPA
p.141 *top and bottom left* CNRI/Science Photo Library; *right* Dr B. Booth/GSF Picture Library
p.148 ZEFA
p.151 NDAA/Science Photo Library
p.152 *left* John Lynch/Frank Lane Picture Agency; *right* David E. Rowley/Planet Earth Pictures
p.162 *left* James Holmes/Science Photo Library; *right* Jonathan Wright/Bruce Coleman Ltd
p.169 *left* NASA/Science Photo Library; *centre and right* ICI Advanced Materials

1

Spaceship Earth

Revision

1.0 Beauty and the Beast

1 Our environment is the spaceship Earth.

Forests contain a huge variety of living things – but habitats are being destroyed all over the world

There are many beautiful areas – but some have become polluted with emissions from power stations, factory smoke and car exhausts

Animals are plentiful in some areas – but pollution poisons many

2 The Earth contains everything that we need to survive, for example: ● water ● oxygen ● food ● fuel ● different **habitats** ● **raw materials** for making things.

3 Water is constantly recycled in the **water cycle.**

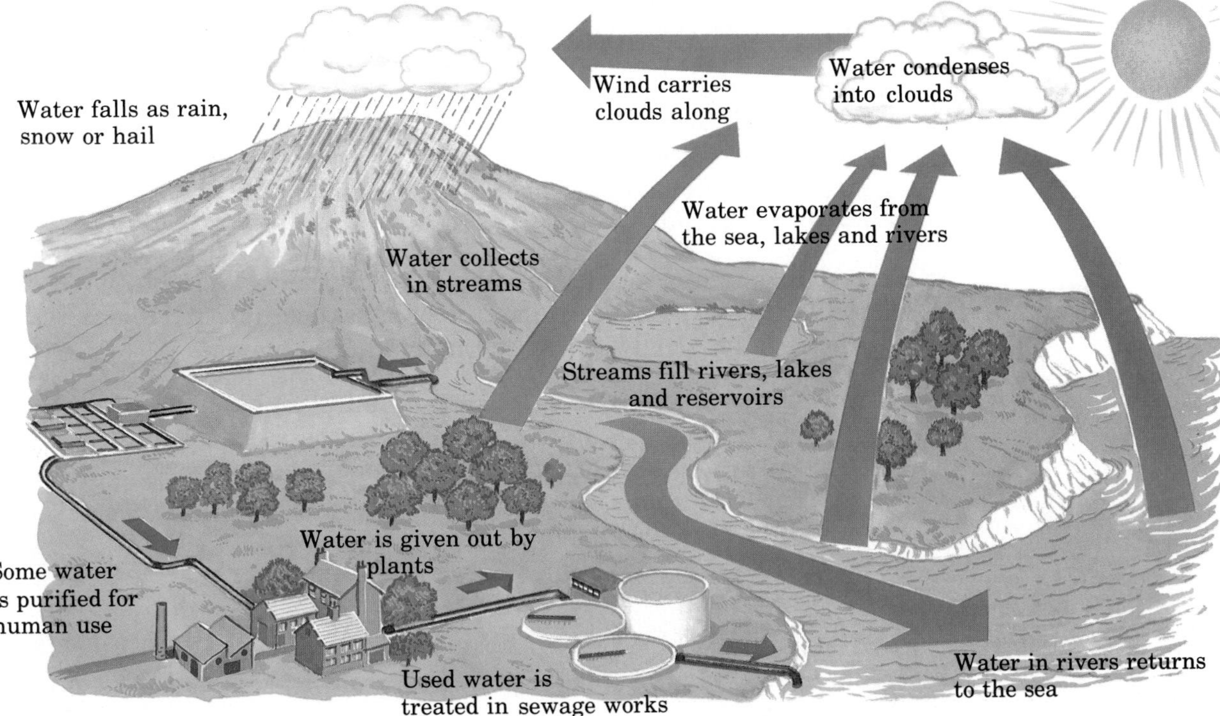

4 Oxygen is recycled through **photosynthesis** and **respiration.**

5 A green plant uses photosynthesis to make food for itself. The plant may then be used by a **herbivore** as food. The herbivore may be eaten by a **carnivore. Food chains** transfer some of the energy of the Sun to every living thing on the planet.

6 Our environment must be carefully looked after so that it is fit for future plants and animals to live in. It should be **conserved.**

7 **Pollution** can affect the balance of the environment.

8 Some waste material can be **recycled**, some is **biodegradable**.

1 You should know the meaning of the words in **bold**. If you cannot remember what a word means, then look it up in a science book (like *Understanding Science 1* or *2*).

Collect and complete a revision question sheet.

2 The Earth is like a spaceship because it must provide everything that we need to stay alive. Imagine that you are in a spaceship many thousands of miles from Earth. Write a poem or a story called *My home is a spaceship.*

CHECKPOINT

Find two adverts for jobs which deal with conservation or the environment.

1.1 Life on Earth

A The animal kingdom

Ecology is the scientific study of ecosystems – combinations of living things (**organisms**) and their habitats. A good start for an ecological investigation is to identify the organisms in the habitat. There are millions of different kinds of living things on Earth. We **classify** them (put them into sets) to make sense of the world.

The most obvious sets are **animals**, **plants** and **bacteria**. Each of these large sets, called **kingdoms**, is classified into smaller sets. Animals might be classified by their common names.

However, it is more orderly to classify animals by using their structural features. Animals are put into the same group if they have certain important features in common. For example, the **vertebrates** (animals with backbones) are one of the major animal groups shown in the key below.

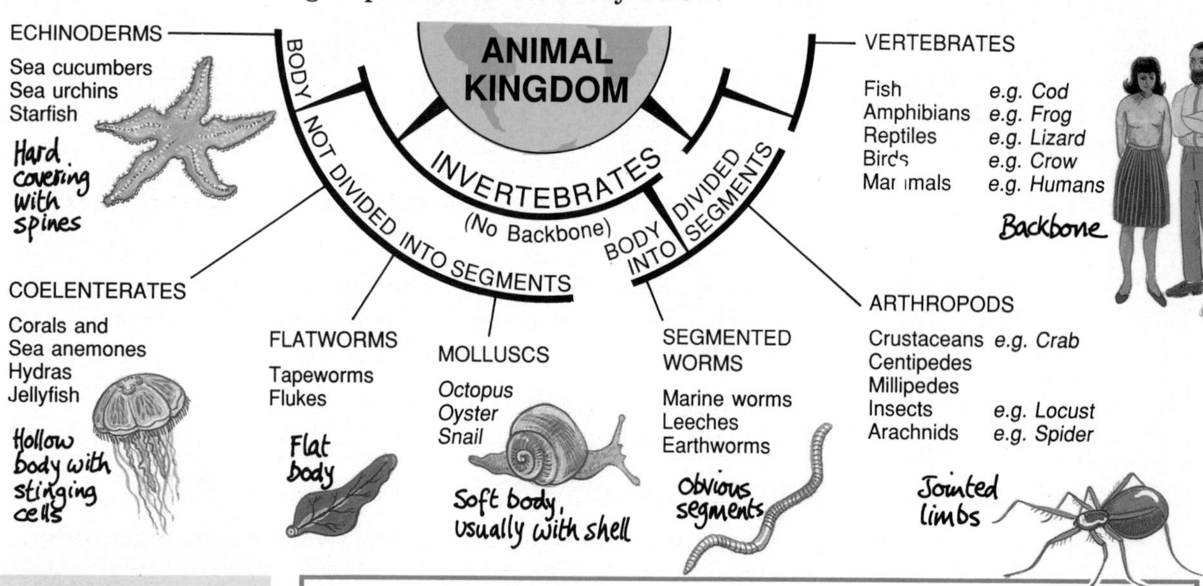

Collect
Set of invertebrate animal cards
Living invertebrate
Hand lens
Animal table

Treat all living things with respect.
1 Use the key to identify which group each animal is in.
2 Record your results in a table.
3 Observe the living animal with a hand lens.

1 Describe the living animal, including
a the details of its structure **b** its habitat.
2 **a** What group of invertebrates is your animal from?
b What characteristics did you use to classify the animal?
3 What features do you think help this animal to survive in its natural habitat?
4 Complete the blanks in the animal table and stick it into your book.

B The plant kingdom

Plants are also classified into several major groups. For example, flowering plants are one of the major groups shown in the table.

Name of major group	Example	Important group features
Mosses and Liverworts		No true roots Simple stems and tiny leaves lacking transport system for food and water Reproduce by spores produced in capsules
Club mosses		True roots and stems bearing true leaves arranged in spirals Transport system for food and water Spores produced in tiny cones
Horsetails		True roots and stems bearing scale-like true leaves in whorls Spores produced in cones
Ferns		True roots and stems, and true leaves divided into tiny leaflets Spores produced in clusters on leaf undersides
Conifers		True roots, stems and needle-like leaves Reproduce by seeds produced in cones
Flowering plants		True roots, stems and leaves. Produce flowers and seeds

Until recently **botanists** (plant scientists) also classified fungi – such as mushrooms – and algae – such as seaweed – as two major plant groups. These now belong to two different kingdoms altogether.

1 **Collect** a blank plant key. Fill in the missing clues and group names. Stick the completed key in your book.
2 Look at the plants in the classroom. Use your key to identify which group each plant is in.

CHECKPOINT

Find out about your nearest botanical gardens, public park or zoological park. Write down the opening times. Describe how **you** would get there. Include a publicity leaflet if you can.

1.2 Adaptations

A A place for everything

The huge variety of animals and plants is not evenly distributed over the Earth. Ecologists study those characteristics of plants and animals that allow them to survive in their habitats. Any living thing is most often found in the habitat where it has the best chance of survival.

Living thing	Habitat	Useful characteristics for survival
Cactus	Dry desert	Swollen stem that stores water Spiny leaves to reduce water loss Huge root system to catch any rain
Mayfly larva	Fast-flowing stream	Flattened body to cling to rocks Streamlined shape to resist water flow Strong legs for gripping rocks
Mole	Underground	Paddle-shaped front feet for digging Short hair that sticks out in all directions to allow easy movement through tunnels Tiny eyes that do not easily get clogged-up with dirt Bristles on nose and tail to sense surroundings

These living things are **adapted** to their environment. Living things that are not adapted reasonably well to their surroundings will become extinct. This may happen when important features of the environment change or when there is competition from other living things for food or space.

Collect a set of dominoes.

1 Each domino has a picture of an animal in its habitat and a description of a useful characteristic for survival.
Play dominoes in the usual way, matching a picture with a correct description.

Collect

Daphnia in a U-tube (corked at both ends)
Dropper bottles of: vinegar, sodium bicarbonate solution
Bench lamp
Black paper
Plasticine
Light filters

2 The behaviour of an animal often helps it to survive. You can see this in action.

Take care of living things.
Change the following parts of the U-tube environment and watch which way the *Daphnia* move. For each change decide why this movement would help the *Daphnia* to survive.

- Dark/light
- Colour of light
- Acid/alkali
- Up/down

***Daphnia* factfile**
Live in fresh water
Breathe oxygen; most oxygen is near surface of water
Eat microscopic green algae
Eaten by small fish

1 Make a table of two columns (*Animal* and *Survival characteristic*) to show how you matched three dominoes.
2 Describe your experiments on the behaviour of *Daphnia*. Include a diagram of what you did, a note of the results and your opinion of how this behaviour helps *Daphnia* survive.

CHECKPOINT

B Design a survivor

1 Design and draw an animal which could survive in this habitat.
Label its major structural features.

2 Describe the behaviour patterns which would help your animal to survive in this habitat.

CHECKPOINT

Habitat factfile
Weather: cold, wet and windy
Ground conditions: steep, rocky and slippery
Food supply: leaves and bark of tall trees
Atmosphere: oxygen, carbon dioxide, nitrogen

Obtain a pamphlet or photocopy information about one extinct animal. Your local museum may have useful information.

A At the top of a pyramid

The flow of energy through an ecosystem begins when green plants trap light energy from the Sun in photosynthesis. The energy is transferred from plants to animals in food chains. The mole is part of this food chain:

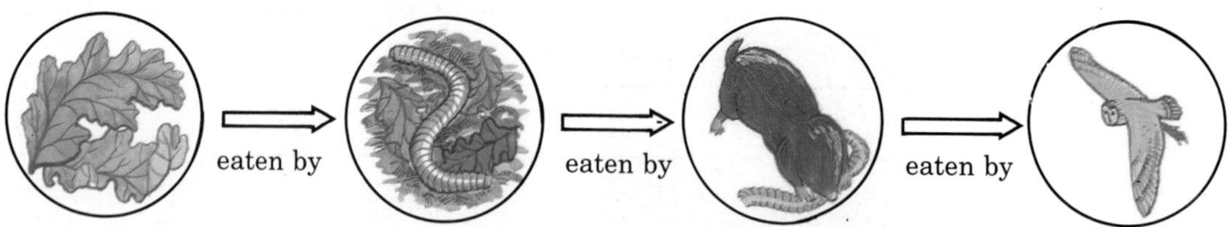

The mole eats a lot of food in one month, perhaps 1500 g of worms, but most of this is not changed into body tissue. If it were, the mole would soon be as big as you are. Only some food is used for growth; other bits are **egested** (expelled) as waste. Some is broken down by respiration to give energy for body heat and movement.

A young mole eats 50 g of food a day. Its body mass changes from 60 g to 80 g in one month

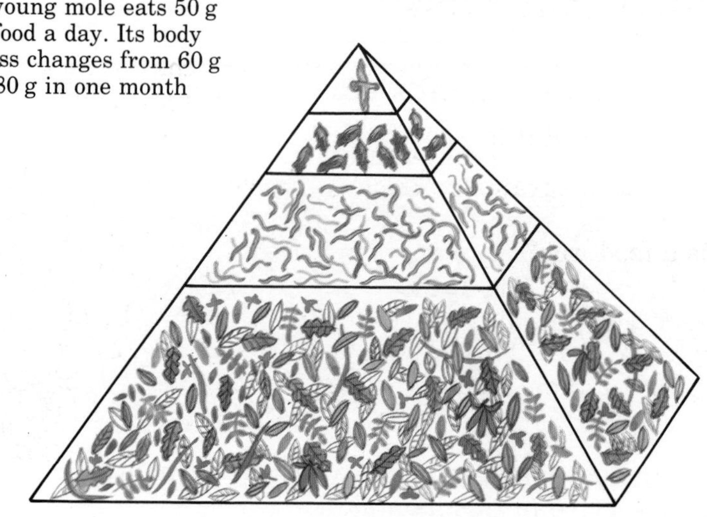

This pyramid is a way of showing these ideas. The size of each layer in the pyramid represents the total **mass** of living things (the **biomass**) at that level in the food chain. The shape shows that only some of the food eaten is changed into body mass. Each level is usually about one-tenth the mass of the level below it. You too are part of a **pyramid of biomass**. You are at the top level (unless something eats you!).

A **pyramid of numbers** has the same shape. The size of each layer represents the **number** of living things at that level in the food chain.

Collect a set of bathroom scales.

1 Weigh yourself to the nearest kilogram.

2 For every kilogram of body mass, you need about 170 kJ of energy every day.
Work out how many kilojoules of energy you need each day.
*Energy needs (**EN**) = (your mass × 170 kJ)*

3 Copy and complete the table below.
For each food, work out how many kilograms would provide your energy needs for one day.

1 kg of this FOOD	contains ENERGY (E)	kg of food needed for 1 day
RICE	15 000 kJ	(= EN/E)
SUGAR	16500 kJ	
PEANUTS	24500 kJ	

1 **a** What is the energy in food used for?
b A week's meals might contain 10 kg of food. Explain why you are not 10 kg heavier at the end of the week.

2 Write a food chain in which you provide the last link.

3 **a** Draw your food chain from question 2 as a pyramid.
b How does the total biomass change at each level of this pyramid?

B Caught in a food web

In real life most organisms are part of many food chains. Food chains are linked together within a habitat. The result is complicated. It is called a **food web**.

Collect a food web diagram and stick it into your book.

1 **a** What is a food web?
b What is the energy source for this food web?

2 Write out three different food chains from this web. In each chain, circle the predator animals in RED and the prey in GREEN. (Some animals may have two circles!)

CHECKPOINT

Find information about at least two predators that live in different habitats in your country. Try to add leaflets or photocopied information about their feeding habits to your file.

Going round in circles

A Food decay

Fallen apples rot in a few weeks

Death and decay play an important part in the ecosystem. Uneaten food eventually rots. The soft remains of an animal decay quickly; even the bones finally disappear. Dead leaves that fall to the ground gradually fade away. Grass clippings rot and change into compost. All living things will eventually die and decay. The photographs show what happens to apples that are left on the ground for a few weeks.

Microbes **decompose** (break down) the remains of living things like apples and bones. In this way they obtain energy and materials to grow and reproduce. Microbes grow best in warm and moist conditions and when the decaying matter is pressed together in a bundle.

1 Make it rot

Use the key ideas above to solve this problem.

Collect a black plastic bag and fresh plant material (for example, cut grass).

Your group has to make the plant material rot as fast as possible.

Design your own method (and remember to think about the important variables).
Set up your rotting experiment and leave it for a week or so. Meanwhile begin your written report.

2 Stop the rot

Use your own knowledge to solve this problem.

Collect five green grapes and four test tubes.

Green grapes are juicy and full of useful food substances like sugar. Microbes on the grape skin will eventually rot the grapes.

Your group has to try to prevent the decay of a grape.

Design four different methods and set them up. Cut the grapes in half.
Use the fifth grape to compare the success of your plans. Just leave it out on a dish. (This is called a **control** experiment.)
Leave the grapes for a few weeks. Meanwhile begin your written report.

CHECKPOINT

B Microbes in a food web

Microbes that cause decay are called decomposers. There are other decomposers like worms and slugs. Decomposers are an important part of every food web because they

- eat biomass that other living things cannot use
- return minerals which plants need back to the soil.

Microbes therefore allow the elements of life, like nitrogen and carbon, to be used again and again. This is called **recycling.**

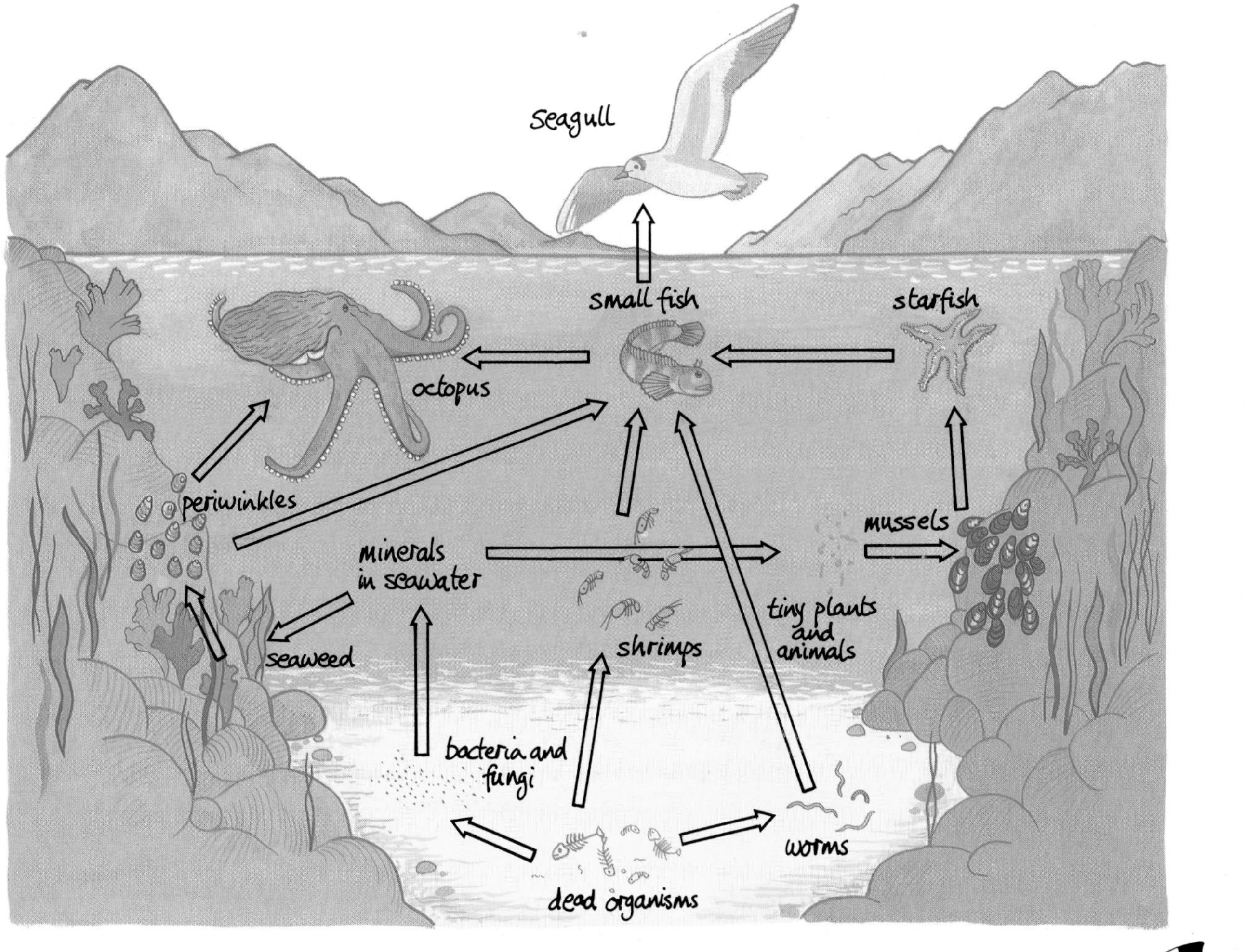

1 Name four decomposers in a salt-water habitat.
2 How do seaweeds benefit from the activity of decomposers?
3 If all the decomposers were suddenly killed what would happen to the number of periwinkles?
Give an explanation for your answer.

Visit a garden centre. Look for material that helps to make good compost. Write down any useful information from the packet.

1.5 Managing the environment

A Protect and survive

People change the environment in which they live. These changes should be carefully controlled to protect the environment from damage, otherwise we will all suffer. For example, we burn fuels like coal, oil and natural gas to provide useful heat energy, but we should remember that fuels can cause pollution when they burn. The fuel that powers a car contributes to environmental damage.

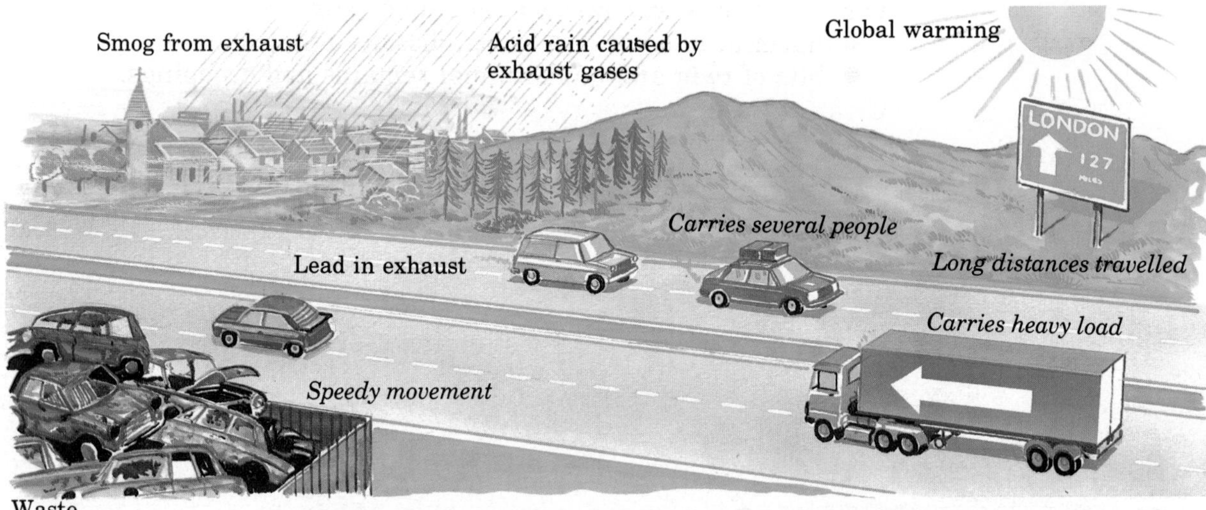

Collect a car pollution card. Each of the activities on the card will give you information about ONE possible pollutant from a car.

1 Choose an activity and follow the instructions. Remember to note your results.
2 Use the books in the classroom to find out what has been done recently to control this pollutant. Key words are: *lead-free petrol, catalytic converters, low-burn engines, batteries, solar power, alternative technologies.*

Write a short report about your activity. Include sentences about the following:

- which pollutant you studied
- its effect on the environment
- the activity and your results
- what the results showed you
- what has been done recently to overcome this source of pollution
- your own opinion about cars and pollution.

B Management of water

Water is a very important part of our environment. We drink it but it also has many other uses. The bar chart shows the average water use per person per day in the UK.

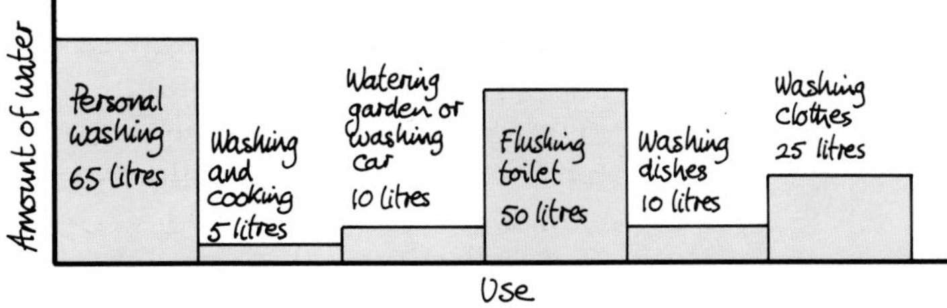

Our water must be clean. It should not contain

- harmful microbes
- much dissolved material
- bits of twig and mud, animal remains and droppings.

Clean water is so important that people are employed to manage the water supply. Your tap water has been cleaned in a water-treatment plant like the one in this diagram.

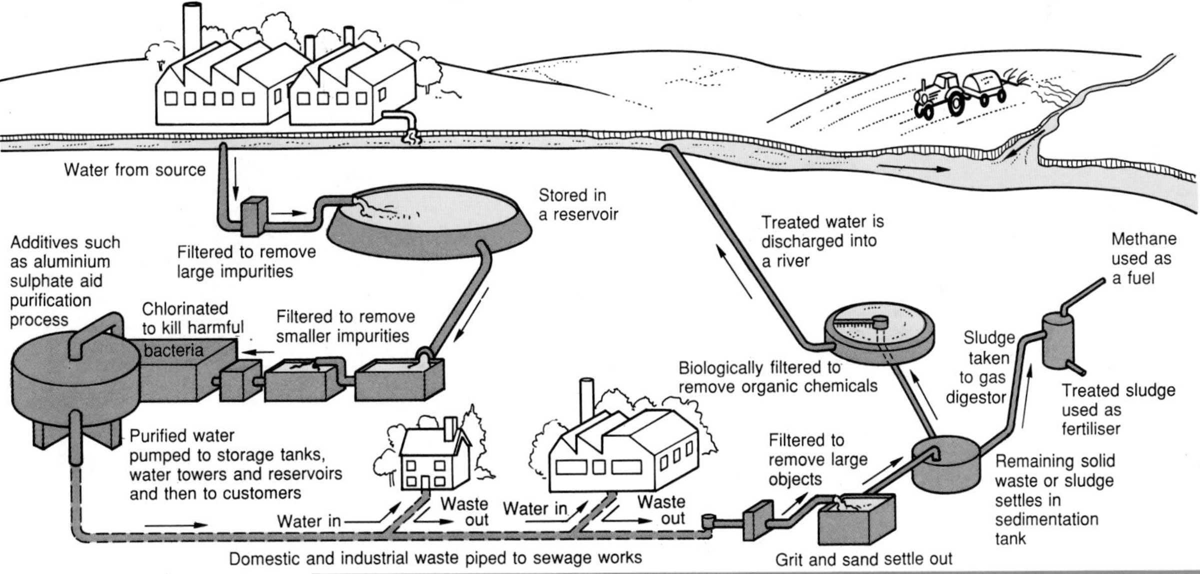

Collect

A sample of river water in a plastic bottle
Water test card

1 Test a little of the water to see how clean it is (use the tests for pH, turbidity, suspended solids, dissolved solids). Keep a note of your results.
2 Clean the water as best you can. The diagram above will give you some hints about methods.
3 Repeat the tests. Note your results.

1 Describe what you did to clean up the river water.
2 Present your test results in a table of three columns, titled *Test, Result before cleaning* and *Result after cleaning.*

CHECKPOINT

Find out the name and whereabouts of your local reservoir and sewage works. Draw a sketch map of their positions.

1.6 Problem

Grow more

Many farmers and gardeners use artificial fertilisers to improve the growth of their plants.
Your problem is to investigate the most effective way to use an artificial fertiliser to improve the growth of peas. You will have to consider

- which variables you should keep constant
- what concentrations of fertiliser you will use
- what control experiment you should set up
- how you will measure and compare the growth of the peas
- the cost of the fertiliser and how to reduce any wastage.

Collect

Fertiliser
Peas
Any laboratory equipment you need

- Work in a group.
  Discuss the problem and possible solutions.
- Decide on the best solution and write down an outline plan.
- Set up your experiment.
- Record the growth of the peas over a week or so.

1 Produce a full page advertisement for your fertiliser (use colour, stencils etc. to make it attractive).
2 Use the results of your experiments to suggest the best way of using the fertiliser.
Give information on the cost of use, and hints on how to prevent waste.

Headline news

Humans have always changed their surroundings. Nowadays we change the environment on a vast scale. We build huge factories to make things, we grow our food on farms, we design roads for fast transport. Sometimes our human activities will have unexpected results. They may well cause harm to plants and animals.

Some environmental issues are headline news. Four examples are given below. Choose **one** of these headlines.

Collect an information sheet and a tape recorder. The information sheet will help you to form your own point of view about the headline. (Is it fair? Is it scientifically correct? What details are needed to explain it?)
Record your point of view about the headline. *Remember:* your tape may be played to your classmates.

Motorway madness?

CONSERVATIONISTS yesterday launched a last-ditch attempt to save a nature reserve from the bulldozers. The reserve is the home of more than twenty species of seabirds. It is being flattened to make way for a motorway by-pass for the congested town of Easthampton.

Rich harvest from fertilisers

Farmers are becoming increasingly concerned over public worry about their use of fertilisers. Some pressure groups have claimed that fertilisers and pesticides are poisoning the environment. The farmers point out that fertilisers are used to produce richer crops of better quality. They also insist that pesticides are essential to prevent most of the crops from being eaten by insects.

ACID RAIN—A PROBLEM TO BE NEUTRALISED

Ministers are meeting in London today to discuss ways of tackling acid rain.
It is possible that new regulations will be introduced to reduce the levels of toxic gases being emitted from factories and power stations.

Safe and cheap power

THE NUCLEAR-POWER industry today hit back at opponents who criticise its safety record.
A spokesman for the industry said "Nuclear power stations are safer than other types of power stations. There have been very few nuclear accidents compared to those that have occurred in the extraction and transportation of fossil fuels."

Times past, present and future

Early humans survived by hunting for meat and gathering seeds, berries and plant roots. They moved from place to place and the local environment recovered quickly from any damage they caused.

However, after the last ice age ended in North Africa and Europe about 10 000 years ago, people began to settle in villages, increase in numbers, and make more permanent changes to their surroundings. They cut down trees to make room for their crops and animals. On the North African coast the once-dense forests disappeared. The cleared land was over-used and became infertile and dusty. Winds swept the soil away and the land became part of the Sahara desert. Some sea ports became so silted up that they had to be abandoned.

Today the effects of human activity are greater still. Our huge population demands ever-more land for farming, more raw materials for industry and more factories for goods to improve our standard of living. These demands cause environmental damage that will affect us all. For example, CFC gases used in aerosols, refrigeration systems and foamed plastics damage the ozone layer which protects us from harmful rays of the Sun. Even if all production of CFCs were stopped now the atmosphere could take 60 years to recover.

Damage to the ozone layer worries most people. Many shoppers refuse to buy products that contain CFCs. This is forcing manufacturers to develop safer chemicals and CFC-free aerosols.

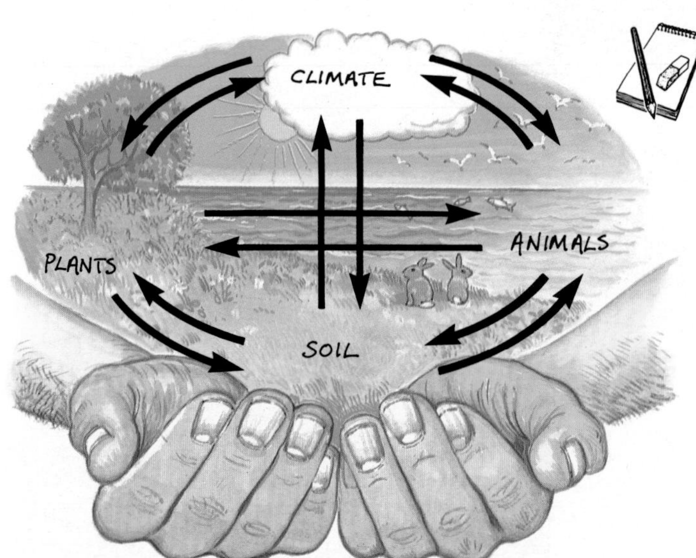

Everything in the environment is linked, and these links are fragile. Once broken they are difficult to mend. The future of Spaceship Earth really is in our hands

1 Why did early humans have little long-term effect on the environment?
2 Why did the human population increase rapidly 10 000 years ago?
3 Give three reasons for the large-scale damage to the environment in modern times.
4 Why are CFC gases important to us? What is one dangerous effect of these gases?
5 What actions could you take to persuade manufacturers to stop producing CFCs now?
6 Explain how human activity is damaging any three of the links in the diagram.

2

Body and mind

Revision

2.0 Health check

1 The human body is complex. This little boy is six months old and is having a health check.

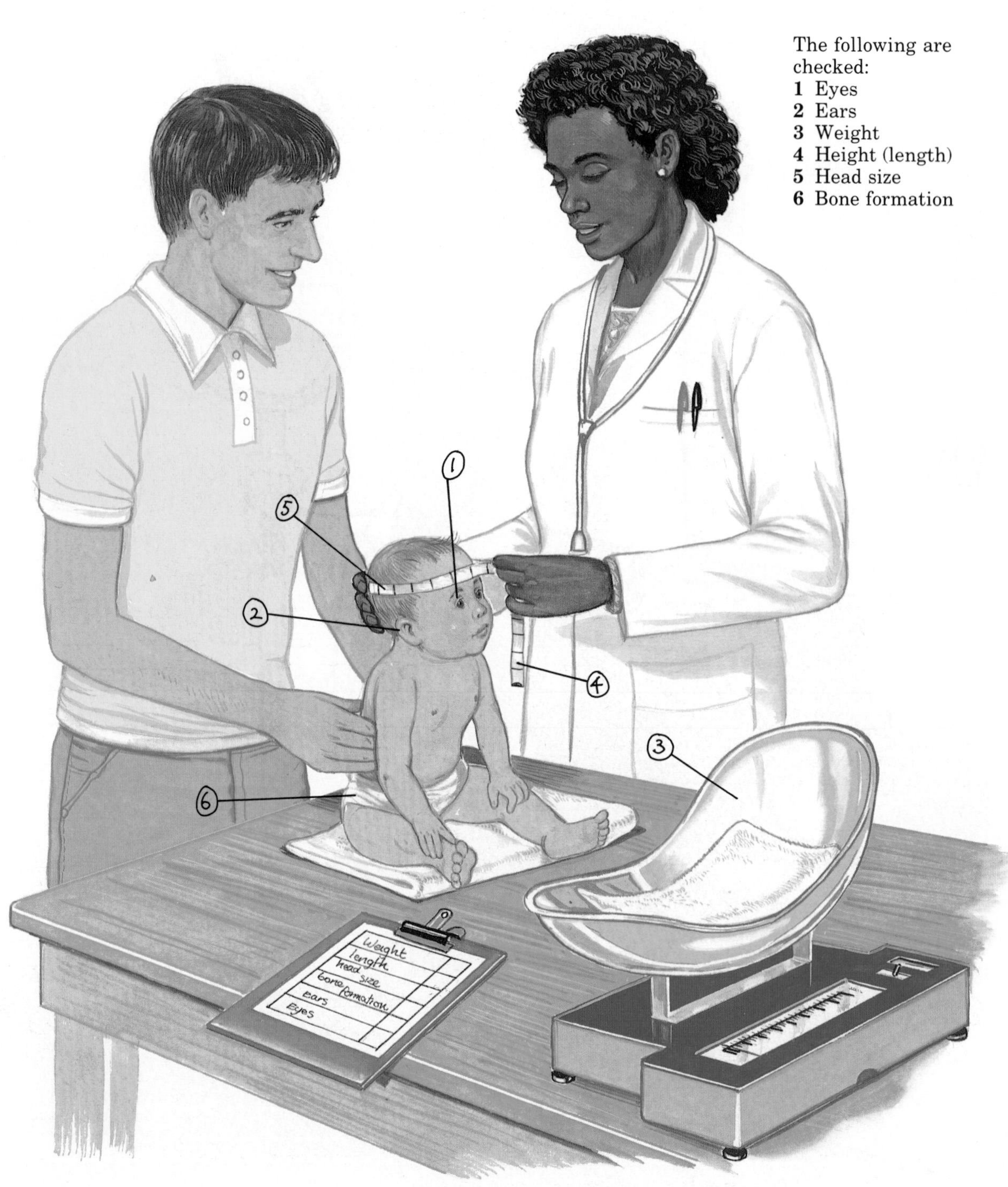

The following are checked:

1 Eyes
2 Ears
3 Weight
4 Height (length)
5 Head size
6 Bone formation

2 The human body is made up of **cells**.
Different cells have different **functions**.

3 New human beings are made through **sexual reproduction**.

4 The sexual organs are part of the **reproductive system**.
Other examples of body systems are the **circulatory system** and the **digestive system**.

5 Human beings stay fit and healthy by eating a **balanced diet** and by taking **exercise**.
Humans should also avoid **smoking**, **drinking alcohol** or taking other **dangerous drugs**, all of which can harm the body.

1 You should know the meaning of the words in **bold**. If you cannot remember what a word means then look it up in a science book (like *Understanding Science 1* or *2*).

Collect and complete a revision question sheet.

2 Health issues are important for everybody.
Your group are going to record a 'radio phone-in programme' about major health issues.
First suggest as many health issues as possible and write them down on a piece of paper. The group must then choose five issues to discuss.
Three members of the group will be the 'panel of experts'.
The others in the group take it in turns to 'phone in' and quiz the panel.

Remember to *record* your discussion programme.

CHECKPOINT

Visit your local doctor or dentist and ask the receptionist for some health leaflets or posters.

2.1 Who are you?

A Variation

Scientists classify organisms by looking for similarities and differences. We all belong to the group called human beings because we have so much in common.

There are also a lot of variations between us. The differences you can see are caused by

- genetics - information inherited from the genes of our parents
- the environment - which can affect the way our genes work. It can also affect the body directly - for example, when you cut your finger.

Genetic variation

Most body features and some patterns of behaviour are passed from parents to child in the form of genes. Genes are like the pieces of a huge jigsaw puzzle. All together they are a complete and detailed blueprint for making you.

Genes are found in the nucleus of most cells. Each gene is a piece of chemical code. The code contains the instructions for carrying out various tasks at various times during the construction, growth and development of your body. Many of these instructions will result in particular characteristics.

Genes are inherited in this way.

Most body cells have two genes for each characteristic

white blood cell

skin cell

① Sex cells carry one gene for each characteristic

sperm

egg

② At fertilisation the sperm nucleus and the egg nucleus join

head of sperm

egg

③ There are now two genes for each characteristic in the fertilised egg cell - one from each parent

fertilised egg

④ The cell divides and an embryo grows

embryo

Relatives, especially long-lost relatives, enjoy spotting characteristics that come from one parent or another.

This happens because a gene can have two forms or **alleles**, called **dominant** and **recessive**. For example,

- attached ear lobes are recessive
- free ear lobes are dominant.

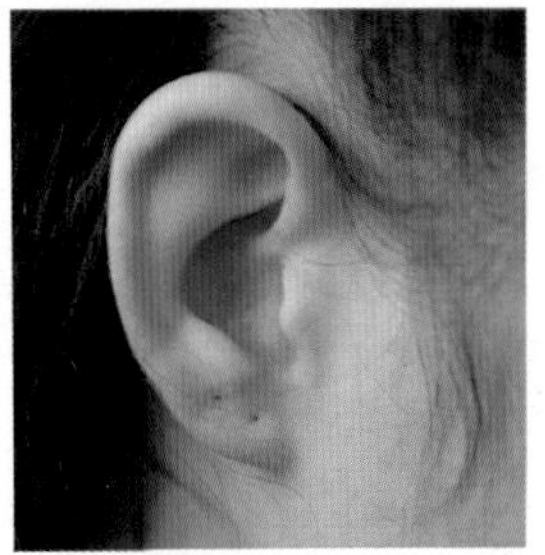

This person inherited the recessive allele of a gene from both parents

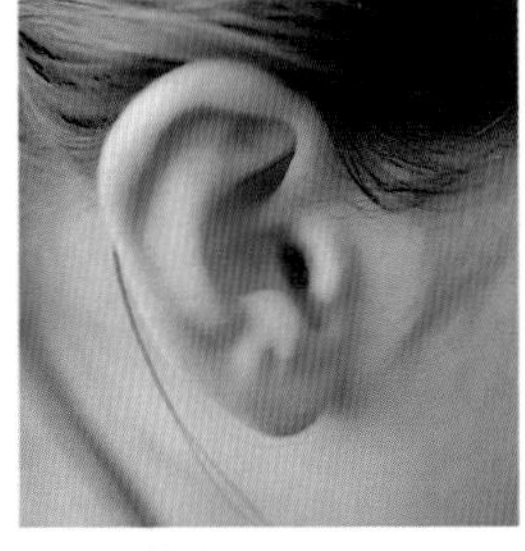

This person inherited the dominant allele of a gene from at least one parent

Recessive characteristics occur only when both alleles are recessive. Any other combination of alleles produces the dominant form of the characteristic.

Some inherited characteristics are shown below.

Dominant characteristics are labelled in BLACK.

Recessive characteristics are labelled in RED.

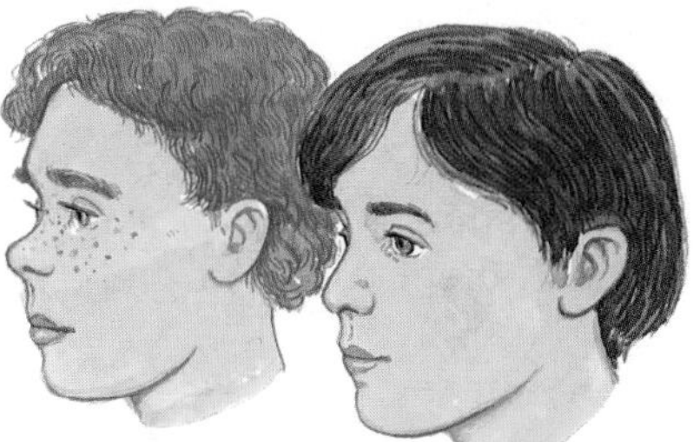

freckles
red hair
long eyelashes
upturned nose

no freckles
non-red hair
short eyelashes
straight nose

widow's peak
straight hair
free ear lobes
brown eyes

straight hair line
curly/kinky hair
attached ear lobes
blue eyes

Some diseases are not caught; they are inherited. One form of deafness and one form of diabetes can be inherited. Most inherited diseases are caused by a recessive gene and so are not very common. For example, one baby in every 1000 might inherit a tendency to develop a form of diabetes.

continued ▶

Environmental variation

Environmental factors can affect the way genes work.

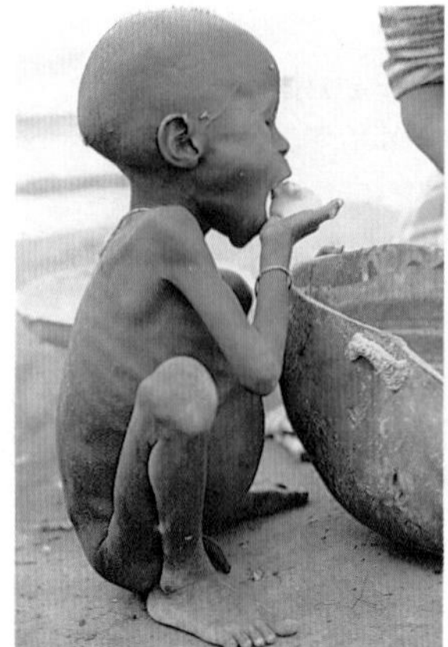

Children suffering from malnutrition do not grow as well as they would if they were fed a balanced diet

These apples all came from different parts of the same tree. They all have the same genes

Weight training can develop your muscles

In hot sunny weather your skin becomes red or darker

Collect

Graph paper
Hand-span sheet

Collect

3 beakers
2 different colours of bead
Coloured pencils
Family tree sheet

Hand-span

1 Measure your hand-span.
Record this on your sheet and complete the class record sheet.
While you are waiting for the class results go on to the *Family tree* activity.

2 Group the hand-span measurements into 15 mm ranges.
Count the number of measurements in each group.
Draw a bar chart of the results, *or* use a computer and graph-drawing program if available.

Family tree

Work with a partner to complete the family tree sheet.
Follow the instructions on the sheet.

1 Make a list of at least six characteristics that all human beings have in common.
2 What does *genetic variation* mean?
3 Write down the names of two inherited diseases.
4 Make a table to describe some of your own dominant and recessive characteristics.
5 What does *environmental variation* mean? Give two examples. Explain how the environment has caused this variation.

CHECKPOINT

B Spot the variation

Look at the examples of variations below. Make a table to show which are caused by genes and which are caused by the environment.

a

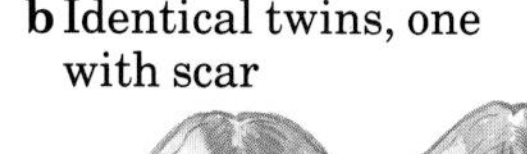

b Identical twins, one with scar

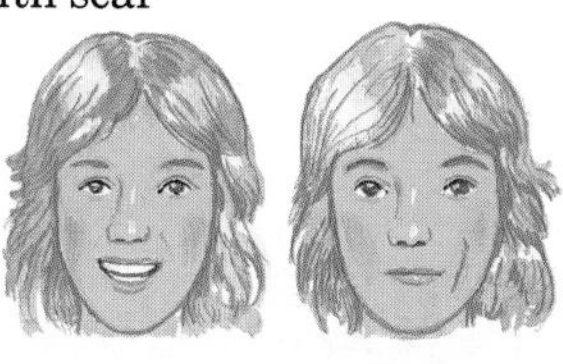

c

d

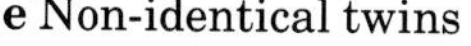

e Non-identical twins

f

g Ben in winter and summer

h

CHECKPOINT

Cut out at least two advertisements for jobs that have something to do with medicine.

2.2 Grow up

A Changes

Growth from baby to adult involves many changes:

- physical – to do with size, movement and co-ordination
- mental – to do with the ability to learn, think and reason
- emotional and social – to do with understanding and learning to control our feelings, and dealing with other people.

Some key stages of development are shown below.

	4 months old	4 years old	14 years old
Physical development	Rapid growth Can sit with support Hand and eye movements co-ordinated	Growing quickly and in good control of most muscles Beginning to catch and bounce a ball	Increasing in strength Reaching puberty Good co-ordination and control
Mental development	Rapid development of centre for co-ordination	Enjoys fantasy and pretend situations Uses imagination Language developing rapidly	Learning a lot of new ideas and values Powers of reasoning and problem solving are developing
Emotional and social development	Self-centred and totally dependent on parents and family	Behaviour depends on rewards and punishments Enjoys playing with other people of all ages Learns to share	Listens to other people's views, can understand rules and regulations Enjoys contact with people of own age

Physical development

1 Copy and complete the boxes of the flow chart below to show the most important physical changes at each age.

Baby → Toddler → Teenager

2 Collect a size-data sheet.
Draw two line graphs to show recommended weight ranges for the heights shown – one for women and one for men.

Mental development

1 What does *mental development* mean?

2 Very few people younger than you could solve the following problems. Work with a partner to get the answers.

a Find the missing numbers.

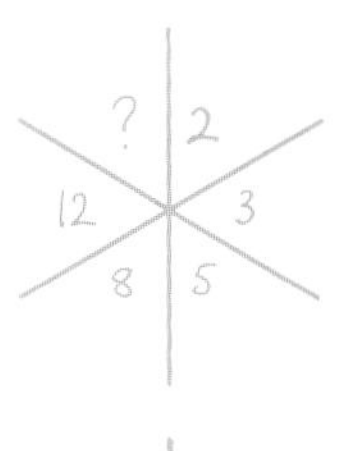

b In what order did they finish the race?
The turtle ran faster than the hare.
The turtle ran slower than the snail.
The hare ran faster than the mouse.

c (i) Move 1 coin only to make 2 rows of 4 coins.

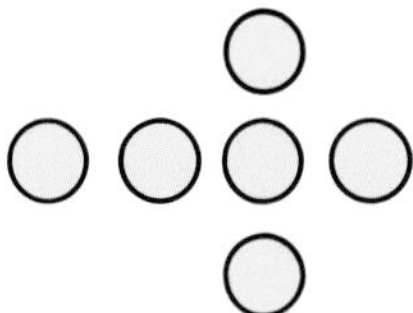

(ii) Move 3 matches only to make 4 equal squares.

B Child care

The pictures below show examples of conditions and experiences that very young children need.

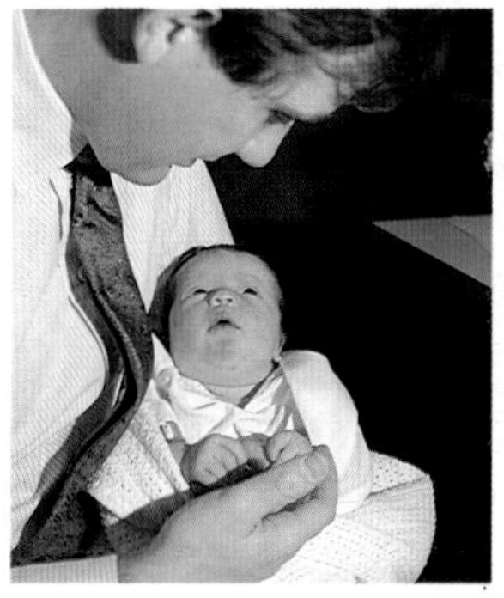
a

b

c

d

Describe how each situation helps in the development of the child.

Find out about your local ante-natal clinic.
Collect leaflets on baby care from your local health centre or doctor.

2.3 Food for thought

A Fat chance

You can look after your physical growth by making sure you eat a balanced diet. The food you eat is broken up first by chewing, then by chemical digestion in the stomach and small intestine. **Enzymes** break large food molecules into small soluble molecules. These pass through the wall of the small intestine and are absorbed into the blood. This food can then be taken to every cell in your body where it is used to release chemical energy for movement and for the growth and repair of tissues.

Some food cannot be digested and this moves to the large intestine where water passes from it into the blood supply. The rest of the food is egested at the anus as waste.

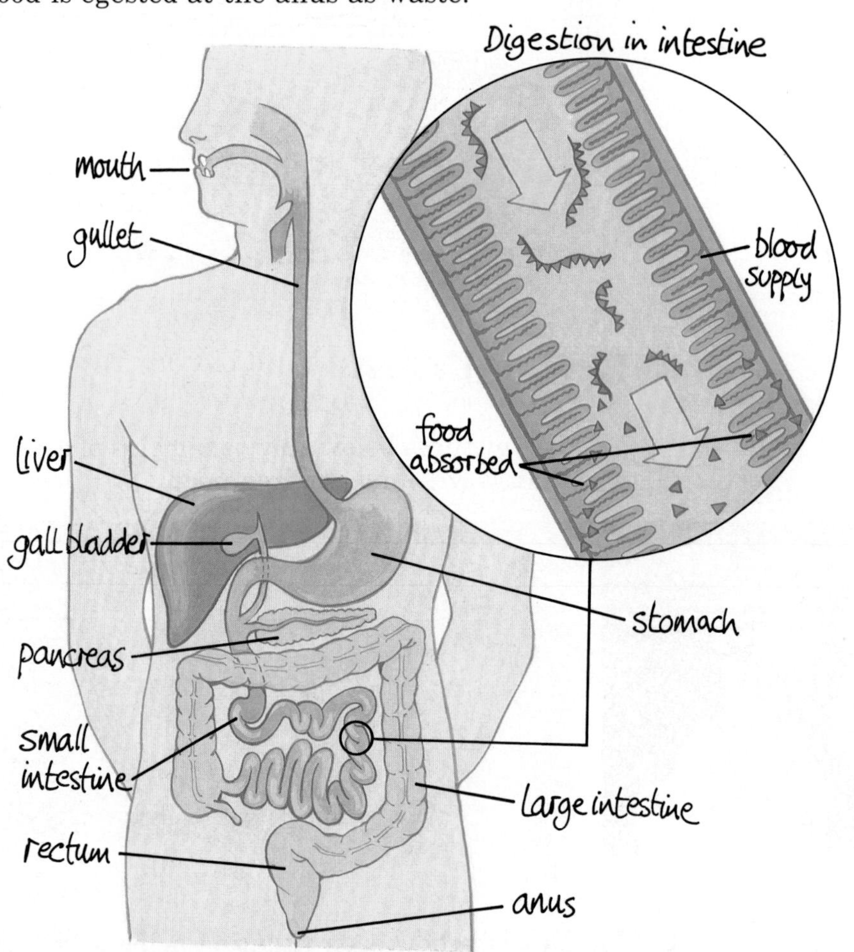

The diagram above shows another two organs involved in digestion – the **pancreas** and the **liver**. Both produce chemicals required for digestion in the small intestine. The pancreas makes enzymes and the liver makes a substance called **bile**. Bile is stored in the **gall bladder** until it is needed.

Investigate the effect of bile on the speed of digestion of fat.
You need to know that

- milk contains fat
- lipase is an enzyme that digests fat
- lipase changes fat (pH 7) into an acidic product
- detergent can be used in place of bile.

Collect any equipment that you decide you need.

1. Make a flow diagram showing the arrangements of the organs in the digestive system. Show where the liver and pancreas are joined to the system.
2. There are 3 stages in digestion:
   - eating
   - chemical digestion
   - absorption into blood.

   Describe where each stage takes place and what happens.
3. How is digested food used in body cells?
   What happens to food that cannot be digested?
4. Write a report of your investigation.

B Model gut

As food moves through the small intestine it is first digested, then absorbed into the blood supply. The lining of the gut is not smooth. This increases the area of the small intestine and allows more food to be absorbed.

Scissors
Sticky tape
3 sheets of paper

Follow the instructions to make a model gut.

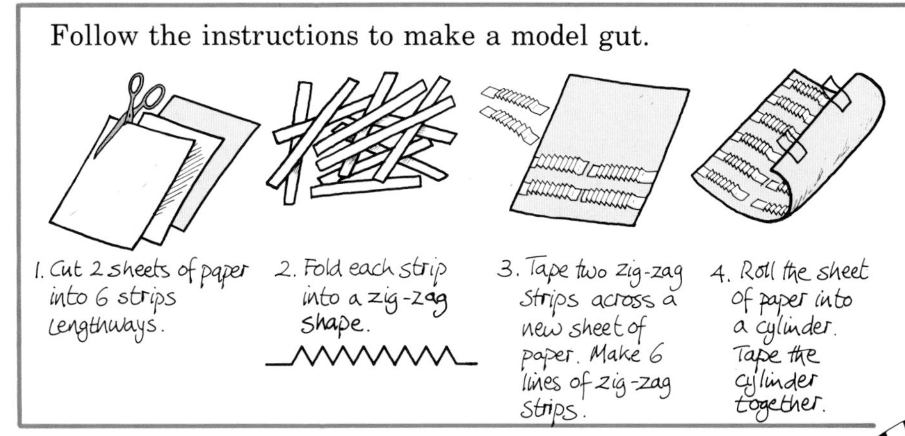

Draw your model. Explain how the structure of the lining makes the area of the intestine greater.

CHECKPOINT

Visit a chemist's shop or look in your medicine box at home to find out how indigestion tablets work.

2.4 See here

A What can you see?

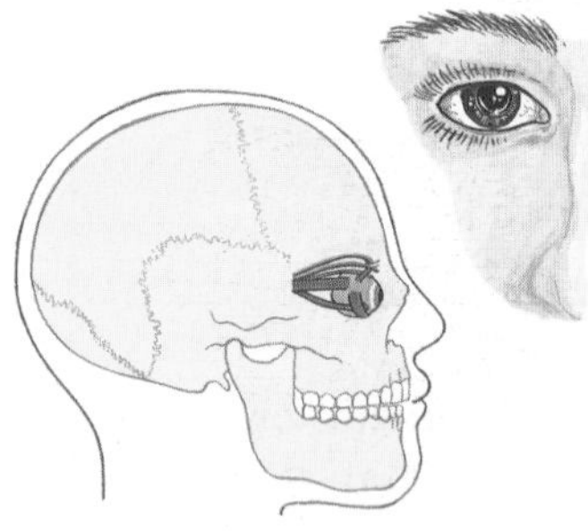

Our eyes help us to make sense of the world. They allow us to recognise friends and familiar places. We watch where we are going and look for clues to possible dangers. We learn through our eyes by reading, by watching experts at work, or by noticing what happens around us.

You may have the chance to dissect an eye. If you do, look carefully for the important structures shown below.

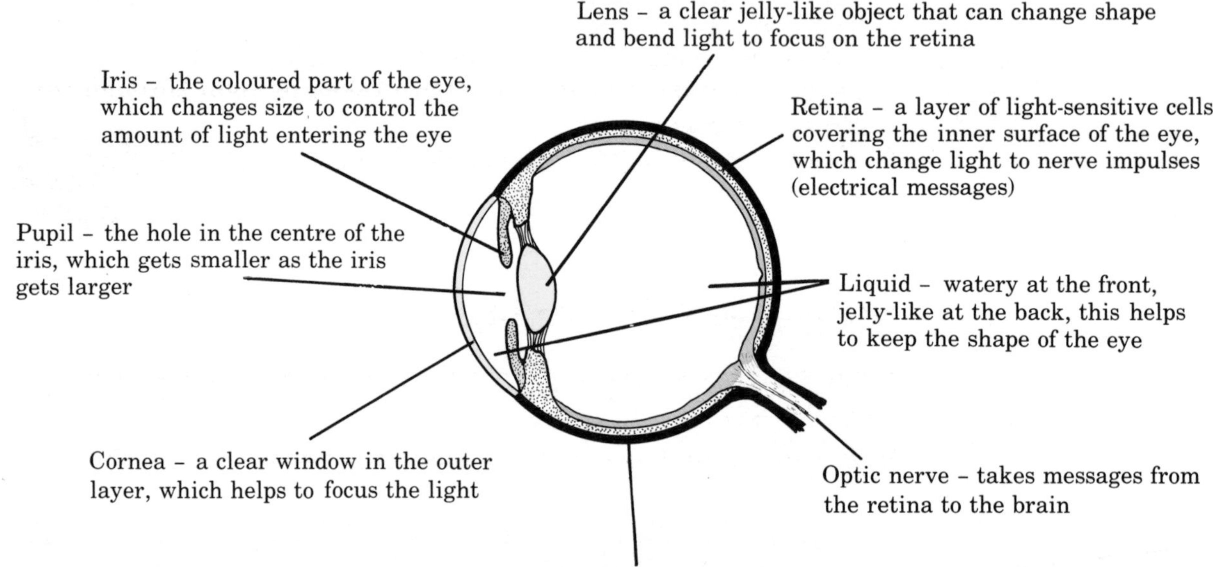

We see an object because **light comes from it** and enters the eye. The light is bent or **focused** onto the retina. Messages are then sent to the brain along the optic nerve. The brain 'sees' the object.

1 **Collect** a set of experiment cards. Complete the experiments with a partner. Answer the questions in your book.

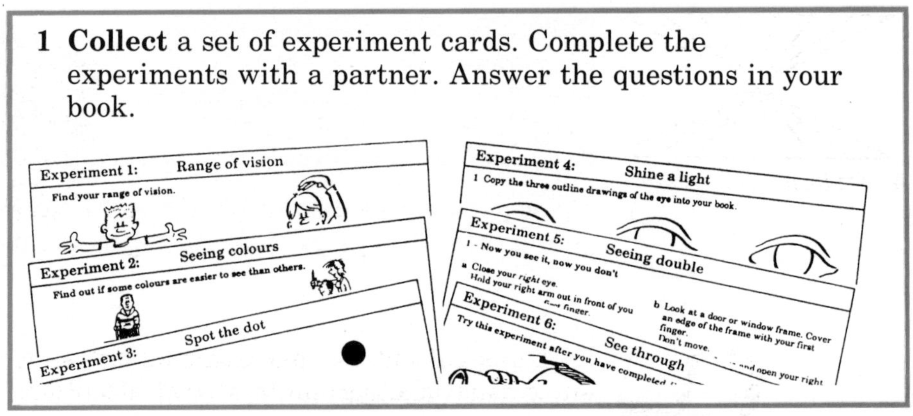

Collect

Tin can, ends removed
Piece of black paper
Piece of greaseproof paper
2 elastic bands
Pin
Glass rod
Candle and matches
Lenses

2 Make and use a pinhole camera to investigate:
- the shape of an image on the retina
- the effect of pupil (hole) size on the image
- the effect of glasses (lenses) on the image.

Make labelled drawings to record your results.

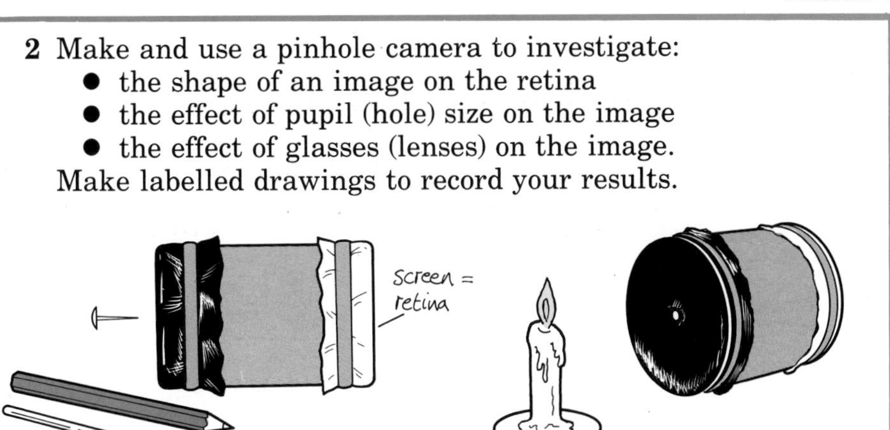

1 **Collect** and complete an eye diagram sheet.
2 Make a flow chart to show the path taken by light through the eye to the retina.
3 Write a report of your investigations with the pinhole camera.

CHECKPOINT

B Seeing and believing

What we think we see and what is really there are sometimes quite different.

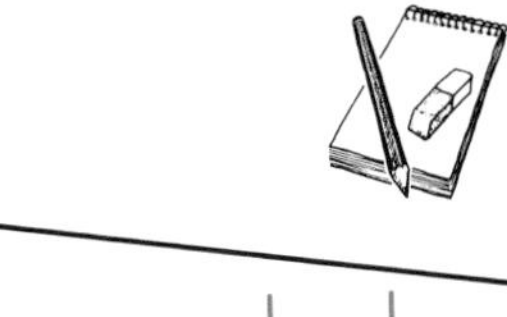

What do you see in each of the following pictures?

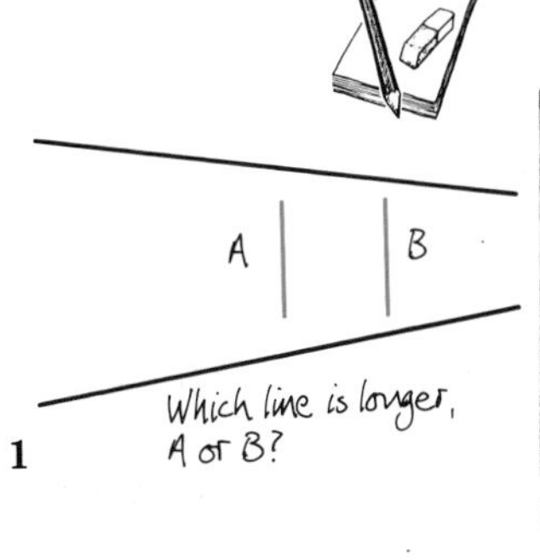

1

2

3

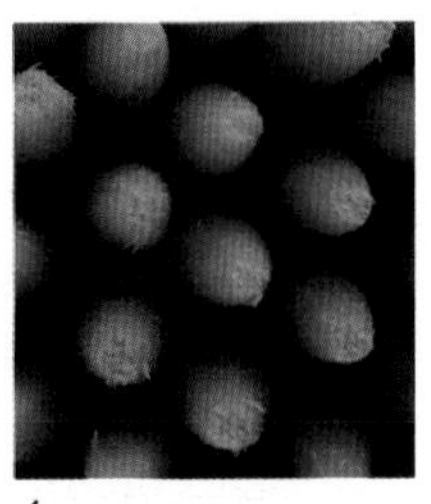

4

5

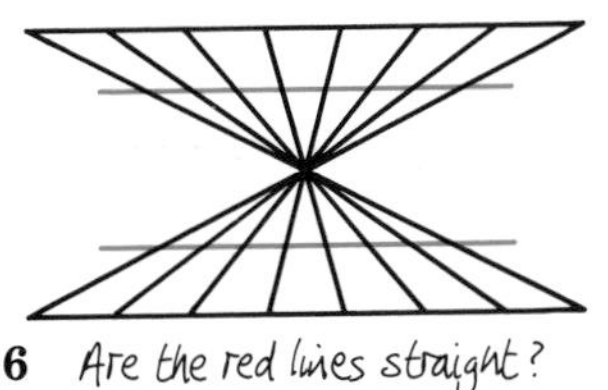

6 *Are the red lines straight?*

7

8

9

Find and cut out two magazine advertisements that use colour or an unusual photograph to attract attention.

A The human ear

Unborn babies love the sound of their parents' voices. A baby will move in the womb to get closer to a gentle voice. As they grow up, children depend on good hearing to develop their speech.

Each part of the ear has a particular job to do. Damage to any part can cause some loss of hearing.

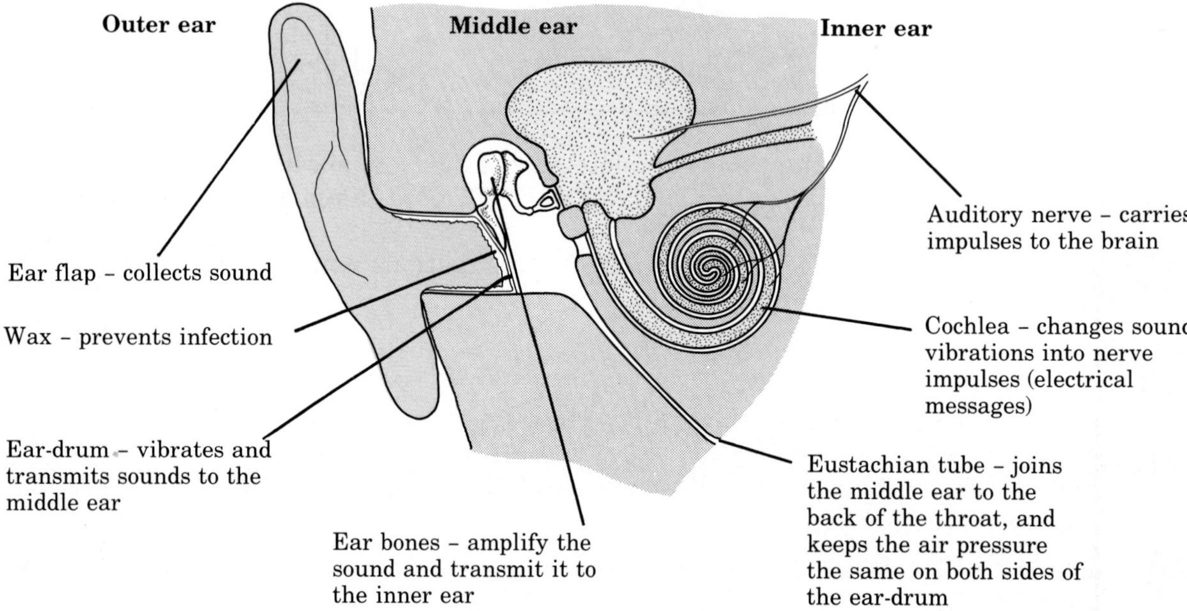

Sound waves enter the ear and strike the ear-drum which begins to vibrate. The vibrations are transmitted across the middle ear by three tiny bones – the **hammer**, **anvil** and **stirrup**. These bones also amplify the vibrations. The stirrup passes the vibrations into the **cochlea**, which is coiled like the shell of a snail. In the cochlea the vibrations are changed to electrical signals which are sent to the brain along the **auditory nerve**.

1 **Collect** a set of experiment cards. Complete the experiments with a partner. Answer the questions on each card in your book.

2 Hearing loss can happen when
- the transmission of sound through the ear is upset
- the air pressure on each side of the ear drum is upset
- the cochlea or auditory nerve is damaged.

Collect and complete the 'Hearing defects' sheet.

3 **Collect** and label an ear diagram sheet.

CHECKPOINT

B Hearing for survival

Explain how hearing is important for the survival of the animals shown below.

a

b

c

d

CHECKPOINT

Carry out a sound survey in your family.
Make a list of everyone's favourite and least favourite sounds.

2.6 Problem

Teamwork

Your own social development can be helped by working together with people of your own age. Work in a team to solve the problem below. You will be in competition with the other teams to find the best solution. The most successful team is likely to be the one where

- everybody is allowed to have his/her say
- decisions are made quickly
- everybody understands the solution
- everyone has a job to do.

The problem
Design and make a structure to transport a marble from its starting point to a cup in exactly 15 seconds.

Rules

1 The structure must be able to stand up by itself.
2 Once the marble is released it must not be touched again.
3 Once the marble is released the structure must not be touched again.

Equipment
1 sheet of cardboard
1 sheet of poster paper
1 newspaper
1 roll of tape
3 plastic cups
1 box of pins
3 elastic bands
1 metre of string
Some Plasticine

Hints
Discuss the problem and possible solutions.
Decide on the best solution.
Make sure that all team members understand the solution.
Draw a sketch of your chosen structure.
Divide out the work, then build and test your structure.

Hold a competition to compare structures.

1 Describe how your structure works. Include a drawing.
2 How could you have improved your structure?
3 How could you have improved your teamwork?

2.7 Talkabout

Making decisions

As you get older you have more responsibility for
- your own health and well-being
- the health and well-being of your family and close friends
- the health and well-being of everyone in our society.

Sometimes you will be faced with difficult decisions. Before you take action you should think about the benefits and costs of your decisions.

What decision would you take in each case below?

Regular dental checks can help you to avoid tooth decay, but they cost money.

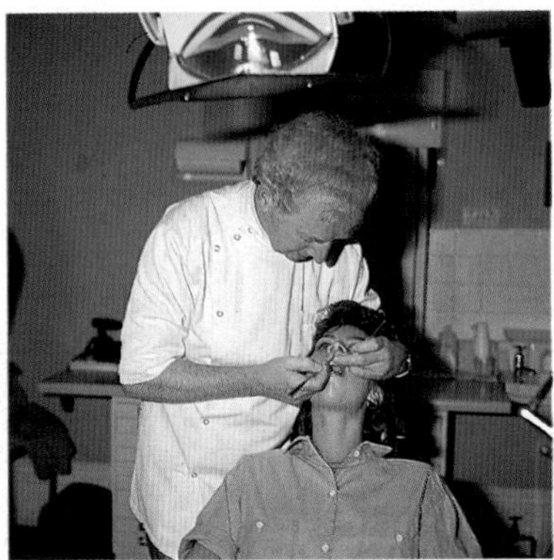

Will you make a visit to your dentist every six months?

You might have a class-mate who is taking drugs.

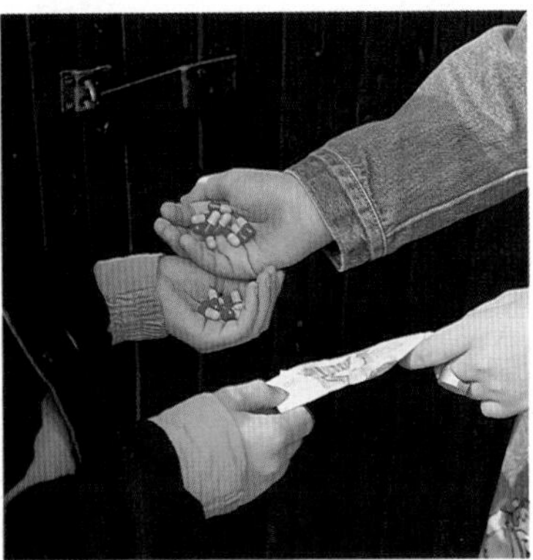

Who would you tell?
(Would you tell anyone?)

When you are at school you take regular exercise.

What will you do when you leave school?

Kidney transplants can save lives.

Will you carry a donor card?

Medical matters

The people below have problems that worry them.

I had my **stomach** removed because I had a bad **ulcer** and now I feel really well again. Why did the doctor tell me I was more likely to get **food poisoning**?

I only get **four hours sleep** each night. I enjoy going to discos and listening to **loud music**. My dad says I'll ruin my health. What are the dangers?

Our doctor advised us to have our child **immunised** against **whooping cough**, but we've heard that the injection might cause brain damage. We don't know what to decide.

The earthquake damaged the **water supply** and **sewage system**. We have been told that there is a danger of **typhoid** and **cholera**. Why is this? How can we avoid catching these diseases?

My mum's always complaining about my **posture** and the **tight-fitting shoes** I like to wear. She says I'll suffer for it in the future. What's the problem?

The doctor told me I've got a mild **viral infection**, but she refused to give me any **antibiotics** to make me better. Why?

1 Work in a group of three or four.
Throw a die to decide which problem you will find the answers to. Books, pamphlets and posters are available.
The words in bold should help with your search.

2 Write a short but complete answer to the problem.
Record the questions and answers as part of a 'medical phone-in programme'.

3

Look and listen

3.1 Adventure into light

A Mirror images

We use mirrors every day to check how we look. Mirrors reflect light from our faces and make it into images for us to see.

If you sit by a friend and look at her in a mirror, she will look rather unusual to you. This is because the image of her face is reversed by the mirror. You usually see her face as it really is. However, she thinks her mirror-image looks normal.

Collect

Mirror
Sheet of glass
2 candles of equal size
Matches
Heatproof mat

1 Tip the wink
Wink your left eye at your face in a mirror. Which of the images eye's winks back?

2 Mirror writing
Place a mirror against these shapes to make the reflections look like a letter 'R' (one of them is impossible to do).

3 A ghostly illusion

a Light a candle and stand it in front of the sheet of glass.
b Look at the image of the flame.
c Move an unlit candle on the other side of the glass until the image of the flame sits exactly on its wick.
d Measure the distances of the two candles from the mirror.

1. Where must you put the unlit candle for the illusion to work?
2. Is the sheet of glass acting as a window or a mirror?
3. Why does the flame have a double image?
4. Describe how you could create the illusion of a candle burning in a glass of water. Try this.
5. **Collect** the 'Mirror writing' sheet. These are two ways of correcting the writing, one with a mirror and one without. Find out how, copy the passage and fill in the blanks.

B Magic glass

Lenses are only curved pieces of glass but they can collect light and form it into brilliant images. A camera uses a lens to form the image of a scene on a screen. When the shutter is opened the image falls on to light-sensitive film and the energy of the light is captured.

You can see the image if you open the back of an empty camera. Cover the back with tissue paper and open the shutter. The image is a small picture of the world outside. It is also upside-down and back-to-front but this doesn't affect the photographs.

Lamp
Lens
Card

In the spotlight

1 Shine a bright light onto a friend's face.
2 Use a lens to project an image of the face onto a small piece of card.
3 Move the lens. How does the size of the image change?

1 Write a full description of the image formed by your lens and how it can be altered.
2 Are the following the same or different for your friend's face and image?
   - colour
   - brightness
   - shape
   - 'way up'
   - 'way round'
3 What two things must you do to make the image larger? Name one difference, apart from size, between the larger and smaller images.

CHECKPOINT

Obtain photographs of your face, and of your face reflected in a mirror.

3.2 Streaks of light

A Working with light beams

If a beam of light, such as that from a laser, passes through smoke or dust, you can see that the beam is exactly straight. Light travels in straight lines even when you reflect it off mirrors or send it through glass.

One way of finding out about light is to experiment with thin beams of light. Use a 'ray box' to make a bright, sharp beam of light. Shoot the beam at different materials and notice what happens to the light.

Collect

Light-beam path sheet
Mirrors
Coloured glass
Aluminium mirrors
Card
Ray box
Cartoon sheet

1 Aim your beam at the different materials and record the light-beam path on the sheet.

A ray box makes a sharp beam of light

2 Marlon wants to use a mirror to send a secret message to Yvonne which the old man cannot see. **Collect** a copy of the cartoon, draw in the light beams to show how this can happen, and stick the sheet into your book.

1 Write a report of your discoveries and illustrate it with your light-beam record sheet. Which surface makes the best mirror?
2 Sunlight bounces off Marlon's face in all directions. Explain why the old man can see his face but not the flash of the mirror.

B Passing light through glass

Shaped pieces of glass can do wonderful things to beams of light. Lenses can focus the beams. Prisms can bend them, reflect them and split them into colours.

Collect

Ray box
Lens
Prism
White paper

1 Send 3 beams of light into a lens.
 a Draw the beams after they have passed through the lens.
 b Move the ray box towards the lens and note what happens to the position of the focus.

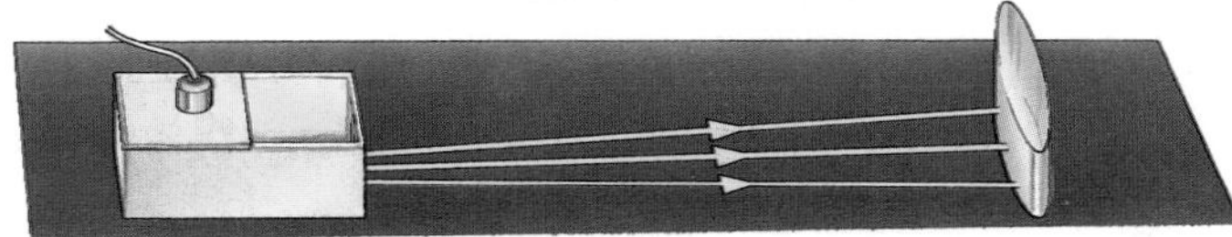

2 Send a light beam into a prism in these three ways.
 a Draw the beam after it comes out.

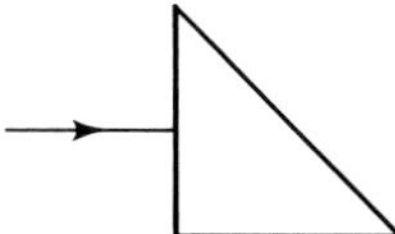

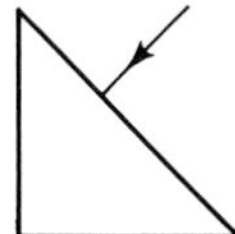

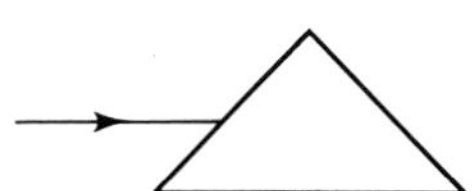

 b Use a prism and a lens to make a bright **spectrum** (rainbow) from white light.
 Make sure all the colours are there: red, orange, yellow, green, blue, violet.
 There should be no white and plenty of green.

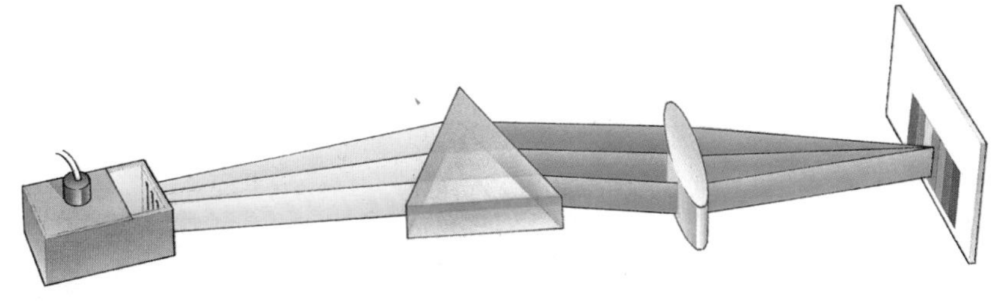

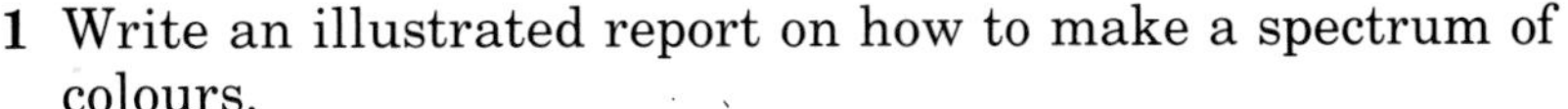

1 Write an illustrated report on how to make a spectrum of colours.
2 A bike reflector is made of triangular pieces of red plastic. Can you explain why it shines with bright red light in the headlights of a car?
Draw a careful picture to show how it reflects the beams, even if the light is coming from above.

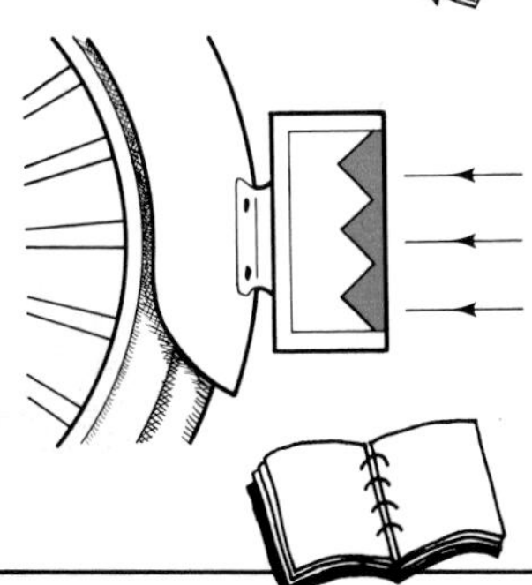

CHECKPOINT

Obtain a full-colour picture of a spectrum or rainbow.

3.3 The sound of vibrations

A Home-made music

Use your body to make some vibrations. Flap your hand rapidly backwards and forwards. The hand moves the air but it doesn't make much sound. Blow through your lips to make the puttering sound of a motor boat. These vibrations are more rapid than the hand-flapping vibrations (about 20 per second) and make a low sound. If you were to twang a rubber band in your teeth the vibrations would be much more rapid (hundreds of times a second) and would make a more pleasant, 'musical' sound.

Collect

Cardboard
Sticky tape
Ruler
Bottle
Water
Tuning fork
Plasticine
Dish
Ping-pong ball
Thread

1 Make the simple 'instruments' shown in the pictures.

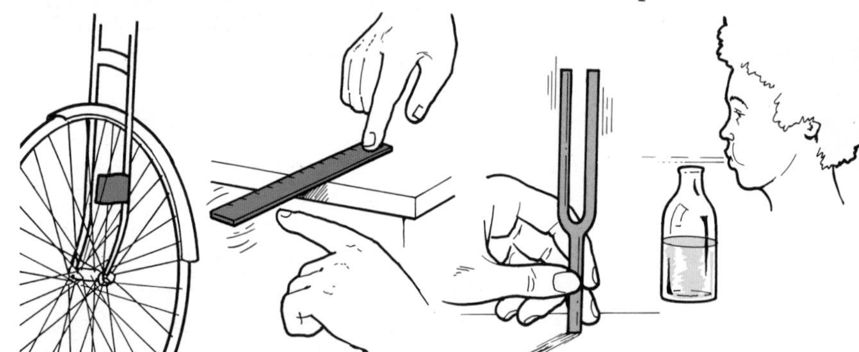

2 Listen to the sound each one makes. Find out how to make it give higher and lower notes.

3 The prongs of a tuning fork vibrate so rapidly that their movement is just a blur.
Convince your friend that the prongs are vibrating.
The pictures may help you.

Write a report in three paragraphs. Describe

- how the rapid vibrations are produced by your home-made instruments
- how each instrument can be made to make a higher note
- the most convincing way of showing up the vibrations of a tuning fork.

CHECKPOINT

B Pardon? Did you speak?

Our ears cannot hear all vibrations. Some are too slow and some are too fast for us to hear as sound.

We often need to know how 'fast' vibrations are. So we call the number of vibrations made in one second the **frequency**. If something makes one complete vibration in one second, its frequency is 1 per second or 1 **hertz** (1 Hz). For higher frequencies **kilohertz** (kHz) or 1000 vibrations per second, can be used.

A **signal generator** is an electronic machine that can make a loudspeaker vibrate at different frequencies. The frequency can be read from its control knob.

Collect

Signal generator
Loudspeaker
Connecting wires

Test your hearing

1 Use a signal generator and loudspeaker to make sounds of these different frequencies:
   a 20 Hz – the lowest frequency that we would call a sound.
   b 15 kHz – the highest frequency an older person can hear.
   c 16 kHz – the top frequency of recorded music.
   d 20 kHz – the highest frequency a young person can hear.
   e 40 kHz – ultra-sound. A sound too high for us to hear.

2 Find some frequencies of your own, such as the highest-frequency note that you can sing.

1 Make a table with three columns. Head them *Frequency, Description, What I heard.* Use the information you gained about the frequencies above to fill in your table.
2 Make a second table with two columns. Head them *Other interesting frequencies* and *What I heard.* Complete the table with other frequencies you found.

CHECKPOINT

Make a chart of the frequencies of your local radio station.

3.4 Sound investigations

A Sound through a stick

When the bell rings we hear it across the other side of the playground almost immediately. The vibrations are carried through the air by sound waves. Find out how well sound travels in solids and liquids. The pictures suggest how you can do this.

Collect
Stick
Small engine (such as an air pump)
Cup
Rubber tubing
2 filter funnels

Ring a bell under water

Listen to an engine through a stick

Use a cup to listen through a wall

Listen to your insides

1 Write a report on your findings.
2 Sound travels well through solids and liquids as well as through air. Can it travel through the vacuum of space?

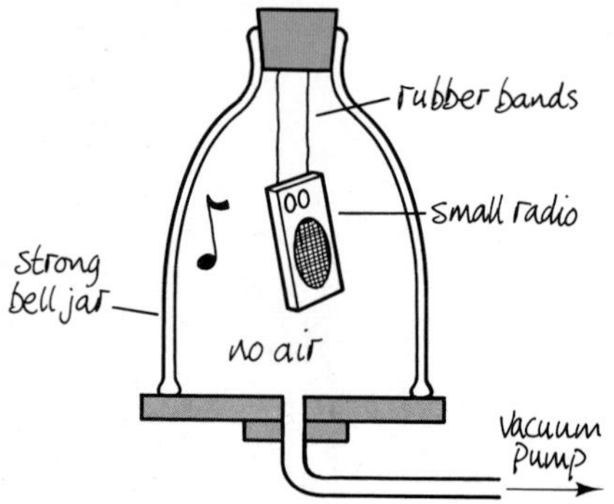

a Predict what you expect to happen.
b List the steps you would take to test your prediction.
c If you can, try the experiment and see if you were right.

CHECKPOINT

B Knock-on vibrations

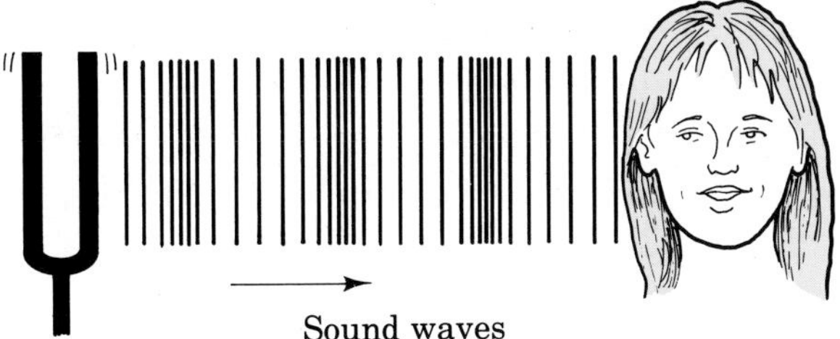

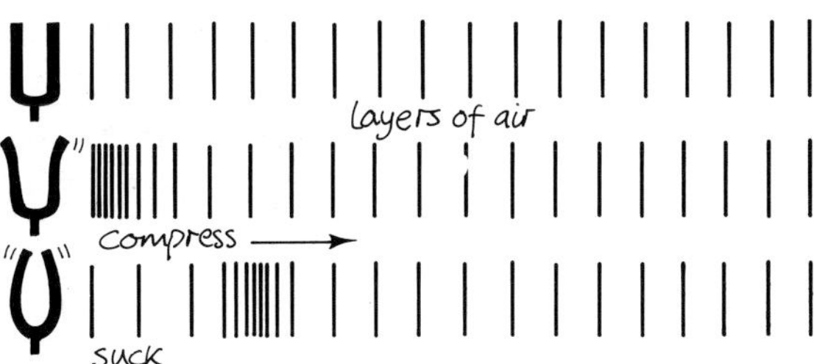

The prong of a tuning fork sends out sound waves. As the prong moves out it pushes layers of air closer together. This forms a 'compression' which moves through the air until it reaches our ears. The vibrating prong sends out compression after compression, bombarding the ear drum and making it vibrate in step with the tuning fork. The rapid moving compressions of air are what we understand as a sound wave.

Sound moves very quickly but it does take time to travel. Here is a way of measuring the speed of sound using echoes.

Collect

Stop watch
Measuring tape

1. Stand 50 metres from a wall that gives a good echo.
2. Make a loud clap and listen for the echo. (It takes less than a second for the sound to get to the wall and back – too short to measure with a stop watch.)
3. Make a second clap the moment you hear the echo. Keep this up, clapping with a rhythm that makes each clap cover the echo of the previous clap.
4. Time 20 of these claps counting the first as '0'. In this time, the sound will have travelled 2000 metres (20 journeys of 100 metres). So from this you can calculate its speed.

The speed of sound in air at sea level is about 330 m/s (740 mph) at 0°C. If the BBC used sound waves instead of radio waves for broadcasts, how long would it take the programme to reach Aberdeen from London (660 km)? What other problems would there be?

CHECKPOINT

Find out some information about underwater sonar.

Noise annoys

Noise can be a nuisance. Other people's noise can make life miserable. Noisy machines are tiring to work with and can damage our ears.

Your problem is to design a box that blocks out the noise from a source such as a small radio or a bleeping watch. The box could represent a room in which you want to play loud music.

Collect together materials that you think will absorb sound – newspaper, plastic foam, egg boxes, wood shavings – and a cardboard box.

Design and build your insulated box. Leave enough space for the radio, and don't forget to make a lid!

Work out a way of testing how well the insulation cuts down the noise.

Give your design a mark out of 10
(no difference = 0, perfect insulation = 10).

Then try to improve your design and test it again.

Write a report (with pictures) that describes
- your design
- how well it did the job
- how you measured the noise reduction
- suggestions for improving your design.

Lacking sight or hearing

Although light and sound waves fill the air, not everyone can receive the messages they carry. The pictures show signs and aids that are designed to help the deaf and blind.

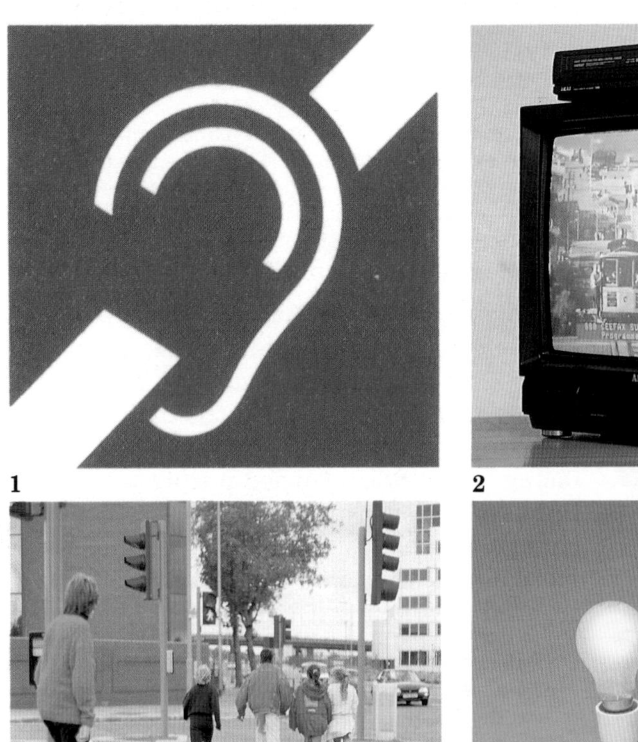

1 2 3 4

Discuss with a partner where you would find each aid and how it is used.

Make a list of the problems blind people might meet in your school, and discuss how you could help to solve them.

Discuss the problems deaf children might have in your school.

3.7 Readabout

The beginnings of photography

The world's first photograph, taken by Niépce in 1826, of a courtyard at Gras, France

Print from the world's first negative, taken by Henry Fox Talbot at Lacock Abbey in 1835

The earliest surviving silver-on-glass 'Daguerrotype', 1837, invented by Louis Daguerre

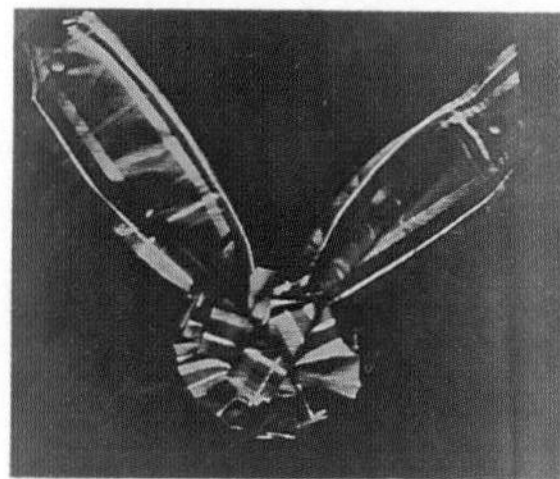

The first colour photograph, taken by Thomas Sutton for James Clerk Maxwell in 1861

In an old science-fiction story written in the 1700s, Tiphaigne de la Roche tells of a long-cherished dream that people had in those days. They wanted to be able to 'fix' the image reflected by a mirror into an instant picture. He wrote:

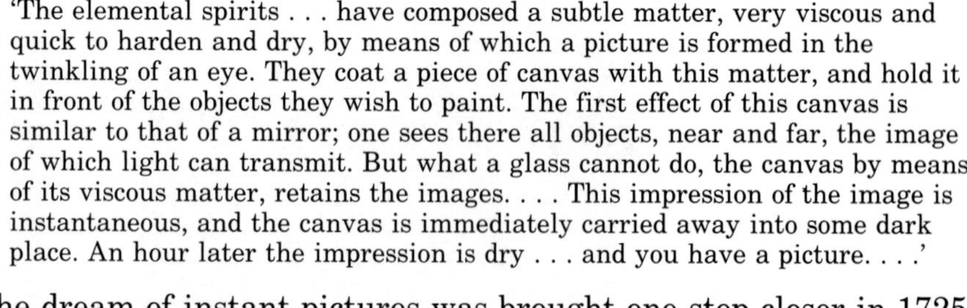

> 'The elemental spirits . . . have composed a subtle matter, very viscous and quick to harden and dry, by means of which a picture is formed in the twinkling of an eye. They coat a piece of canvas with this matter, and hold it in front of the objects they wish to paint. The first effect of this canvas is similar to that of a mirror; one sees there all objects, near and far, the image of which light can transmit. But what a glass cannot do, the canvas by means of its viscous matter, retains the images. . . . This impression of the image is instantaneous, and the canvas is immediately carried away into some dark place. An hour later the impression is dry . . . and you have a picture. . . .'

The dream of instant pictures was brought one step closer in 1725 by Professor Johann Schultze. He was trying to make phosphorus by mixing chalk and nitric acid. The acid happened to contain some silver. He performed the experiment near an open window in the sunshine and was surprised to see that the side of the flask facing the window turned purple while the portion away from the light remained white. Tests by the fire proved that the colour change was not due to heat. When he used a mixture containing more silver, the colour appeared more quickly. Then Schultze covered the flask with paper from which he had cut out letters.

> 'Before long I found that the sun's rays on the side on which they had touched the glass through the apertures in the paper, wrote the words . . . so accurately and distinctly on the chalk sediment, that many people . . . were led to attribute the result to all kinds of artifices.'

Schultze had discovered by accident that silver nitrate, made from the silver and nitric acid, was sensitive to light and could capture images.

Other scientists carried on the search for the 'subtle viscous matter that can form a picture in the twinkling of an eye', but it wasn't until 1826 that the world's first photograph was taken. This needed an exposure of 8 hours. Nowadays photographic film and paper are so sensitive that they can capture the 'mirror image' in a split second. However they are so cheap and easy to use that we can forget how much patient scientific work was needed to invent them.

1. Draw a picture of the experiment Schultze did in the sun.
2. Describe three things that Schultze did during his experiment that all good scientists should do.

4

Back to Earth

Revision 4.0 Restless Earth

1 The Earth is one of the planets in the **solar system**.

2 Seen from the Earth, the Moon appears to change its shape during each month. The different shapes are called the **phases of the Moon**.

3 Our planet Earth is a place of great natural beauty and a place of constant physical change.

Volcanoes erupt, spewing lava which solidifies to produce new rock formations

Water dripping from the ceilings of limestone caves builds up deposits of exotic shapes

Glaciers erode valleys and transport material

Earthquakes, such as the one in California in October 1989, cause great devastation

4 Movements of the **Earth's crust** have slowly created **landforms** such as mountain ranges.
Sudden changes to the landscape can be caused by **volcanoes** and **earthquakes**.

5 The three main types of rock are **igneous, sedimentary** and **metamorphic.**

6 The surface of the Earth is constantly **weathered** by sun, wind, rain and frost. Loose fragments are carried away or **eroded**.

7 **Fossils** can form in several different ways. Scientists study fossils to deduce what the Earth was like millions of years ago.

Loose fragments of rock broken off by weathering fall to the foot of the mountain, forming a steep eroded slope

Plant fossil

Fossil skulls of early human ancestors

Excavator carefully removing a stegosaurus leg bone from a cliff

1 You should know the meaning of the words in **bold**.
If you cannot remember what a word means then look it up in a science book (like *Understanding Science 1* or *2*).

Collect and complete a revision question sheet.

2 Imagine that you are a reporter on the scene of an erupting volcano. What would it look, smell and sound like?
You must get your story out quickly. You can;

- type it on a word processor, or
- telephone it to your editor, or
- write it out.

4.1 The mysterious universe

A Where am I?

The Hubble space telescope

When you look up at the night sky you can see thousands of stars in one tiny corner of the universe. Although we are learning more about the universe all the time, many questions remain. How did the universe form? How big is it? Are there any other living creatures out there? What is our place in the universe?

The universe

Scientists hope that spacecraft such as the Hubble telescope, launched in 1990, will provide some of the answers by sending pictures back to Earth of distant parts of our mysterious universe.

We inhabit Earth, a small blue-green planet going round a medium-sized star that we call the Sun. This star is one of at least 100 000 million in a **galaxy** called the **Milky Way**. The Sun is near the outer edge of this galaxy and there are about 10 000 million galaxies in the universe.

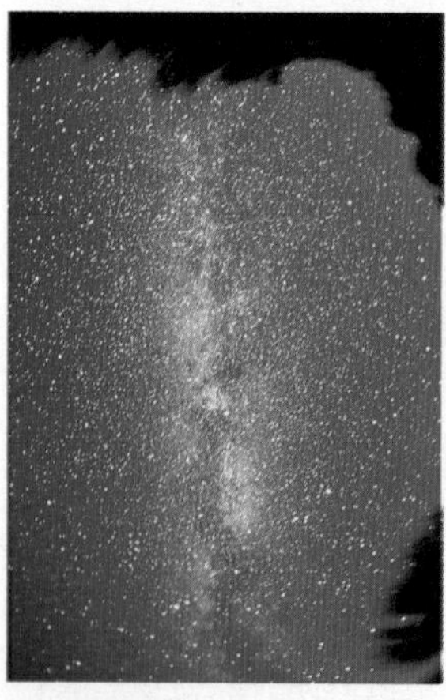
The Milky Way

Distances in the universe are so vast that they are measured in **light years** (the distance light travels in one year) rather than km. The Sun is 8.3 **light minutes** (about 150 million km) away, so light from the Sun takes 8.3 minutes to reach us. The next nearest star, Proxima Centauri, is 4.22 light years away. If a spaceship could travel at the speed of light it would take 4.22 years to reach this star. *Voyager I*, a spacecraft launched in 1977, moves much slower than light. It would take 40 000 years to reach Proxima Centauri!

Our galaxy, the Milky Way, is about 100 000 light years across! From Earth's position towards the edge of the Milky Way the rest of our galaxy looks like a hazy band in the clear night sky.

The universe — The Milky Way — The solar system — Earth

The solar system

Some of the objects visible in the night sky are closer to home. The Moon and planets are part of the solar system. We can see them at night because light from the Sun is reflected off them. The solar system is described in the diagrams, table and bar chart below. Each planet takes a path called an **orbit** around the Sun. The time taken to complete one orbit is called one **revolution**.

Planet	Colour	1 revolution
Mercury	pink	88 days
Venus	white	225 days
Earth	blue/white	1 year
Mars	red	687 days
Jupiter	orange	11.9 years
Saturn	yellow	29.5 years
Neptune	blue/green	165 years
Uranus	green	84 years
Pluto	brown	248 years

Scale: 1 cm = 200 000 km

Sun

Jupiter

Saturn

The relative sizes of the Sun and the two largest planets, Jupiter and Saturn

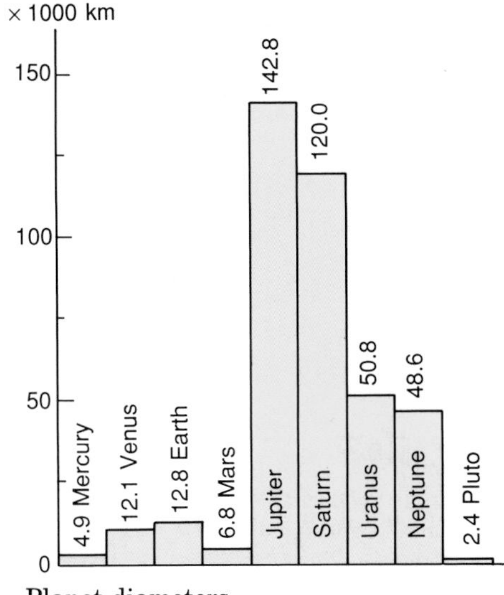

Planet diameters

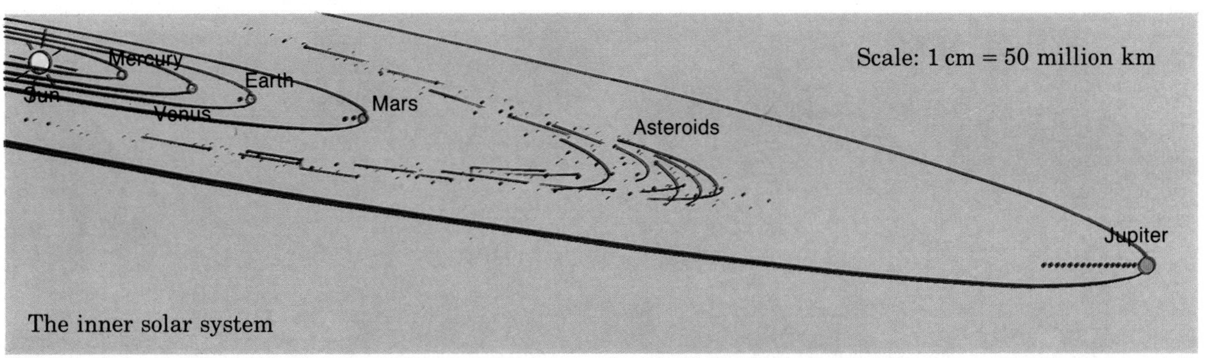

The inner solar system

The outer solar system

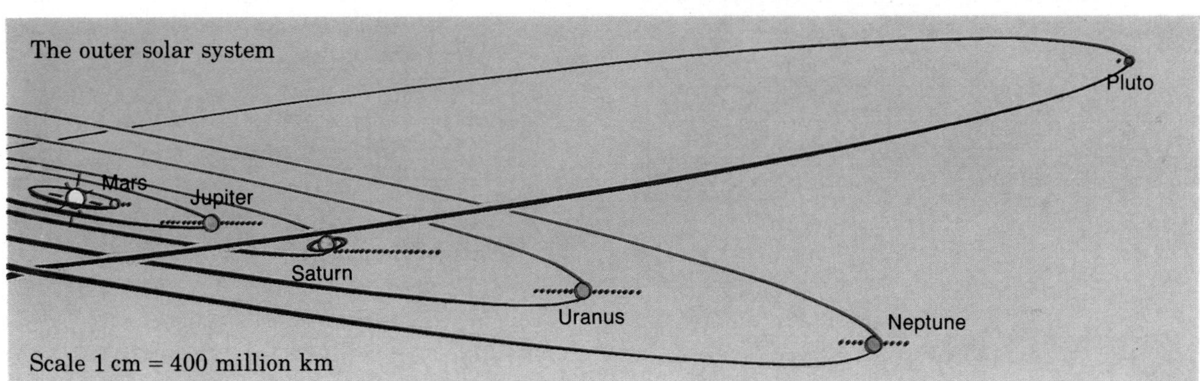

Scale 1 cm = 400 million km

continued ▶

The Earth's orbit

The Earth spins or **rotates** from west to east as it orbits the Sun. It is also tilted at an angle as it spins. This explains why we experience

- night and day
- seasons.

Night and day

The Earth makes one complete rotation every 24 hours. So at any one time half of the planet is facing the Sun and is in daylight. The other half is hidden from the Sun and it is night time there.

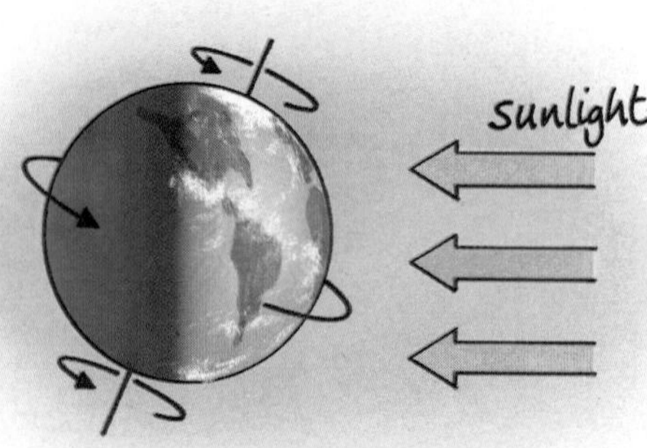

The seasons

The northern hemisphere is tilted towards the Sun during its summer, so the Sun is high in the sky on its summer days. In its winter the northern hemisphere is tilted away from the Sun, so the Sun is low in the sky throughout its winter.

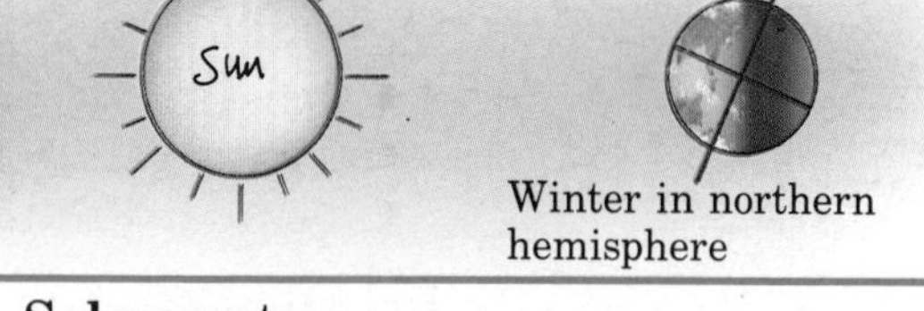

Summer in northern hemisphere

Winter in northern hemisphere

Solar system sheet
Earth orbit sheet
Scissors
2 paper fasteners
Coloured pencils

Solar system

1 Make the solar-system disc (follow the instructions on the sheet).
2 Use the information in this topic to complete the disc. Stick it into your book.

Earth orbit

1 Make the model of Earth's orbit.
2 Discuss with a partner how the model can be used to demonstrate
   - why we have night and day
   - the reason for having different seasons
   - why temperature and day-length should be different in summer and winter.
3 Complete the information on the model. Stick it into your book.

1 Describe the position of planet Earth in the universe.
2 Use class or library books to write a report about the mysterious canals on Mars. Words and names to look up in an index are *Giovanni Schiaparelli, Percival Lowell, Mariner, Viking.*

CHECKPOINT

B Heavenly effects

The movement of Sun and Moon have certain other effects on Earth and produce some interesting sights.

High tide and low tide in the Severn estuary. Tides are caused by the gravitational pull of the Sun and Moon

Charged particles produced by the Sun cause the Northern (and Southern) Lights

Solar eclipses occur when the Earth, Moon and Sun are lined up

Collect

Bulb
Battery
2 connecting wires
2 balls

Make a model to investigate the various ways that the Sun, Moon and Earth could line up. Use the

- bulb to represent the Sun
- larger ball to represent the Earth
- smaller ball to represent the Moon.

Hold the 'Earth' in one hand. As you walk around the 'Sun' move the 'Moon' around the 'Earth'.

Discuss

1 Which positions would cause the highest and lowest tides.
2 Which positions cause an eclipse of the Moon and of the Sun.
3 How the phases of the Moon are produced.

1 Describe three effects of the Sun and Moon that can be seen from Earth.
2 Draw the positions of the Sun, Moon and Earth that would produce
   - highest and lowest tides
   - an eclipse of the Sun
   - an eclipse of the Moon.
3 Draw a diagram to show how the phases of the Moon are produced.

Find out about the location and opening times of your nearest observatory or planetarium, or about a local astronomy club, or watch a TV programme about astronomy.

4.2 Rock groups

A Types of rock

The rocks that you can pick up on a beach, on a mountain or in the garden are all made up of a combination of chemical compounds called **minerals**. There are three main types of rock; **igneous**, **sedimentary** and **metamorphic**. The rock cycle shows how new rock is formed over long time periods by processes on the Earth's surface and by processes deep within the Earth.

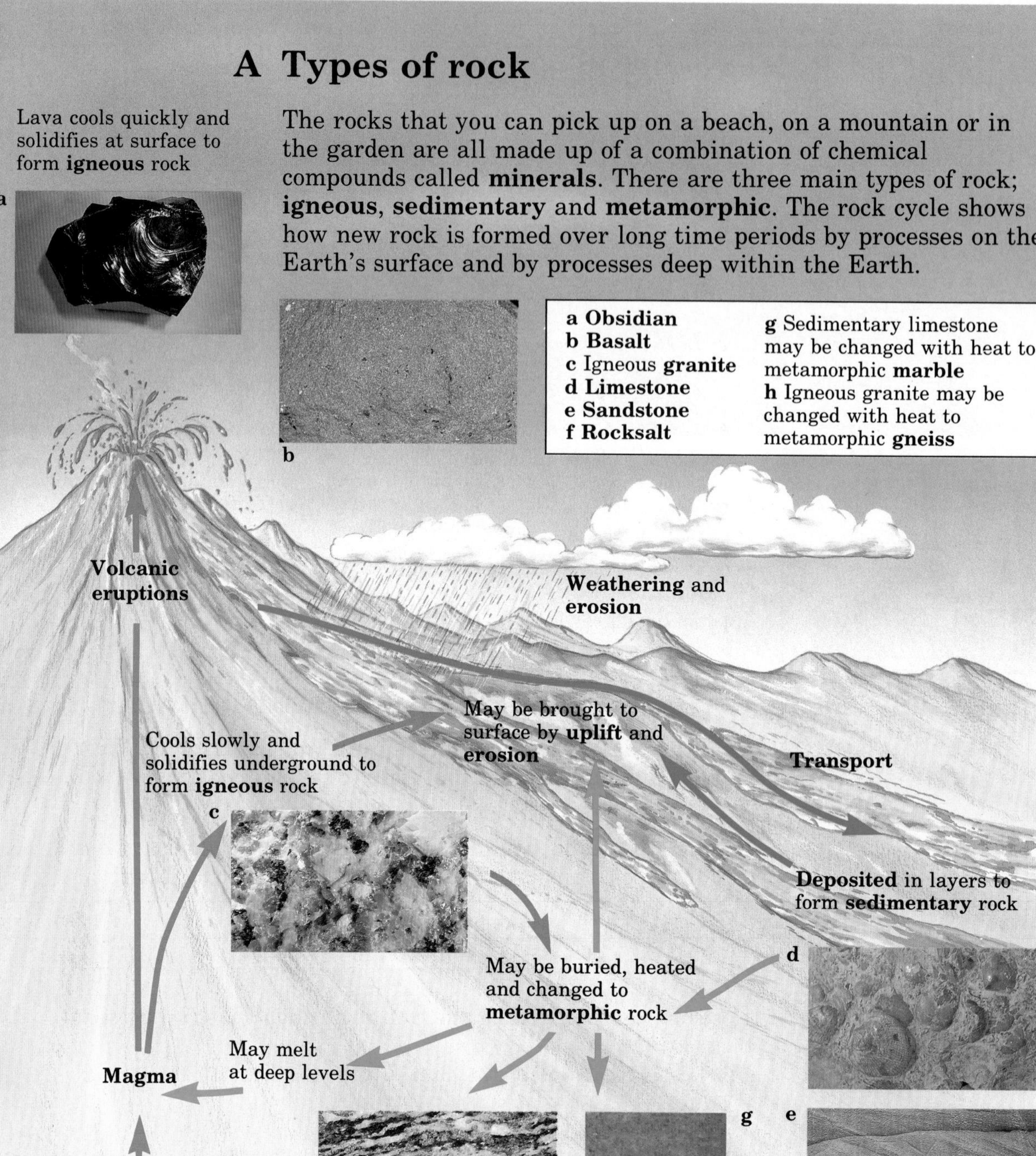

Key

Igneous rocks
Sedimentary rocks
Metamorphic rocks

Collect
Large jar
Soil sample
Ruler

The following activities use models to show how rock types form

Sedimentary rocks

1. Add water to jar until it is ⅔ full. Measure the depth of water.
2. Pour the soil sample into the jar and swirl it gently. Allow the soil to settle.
3. Measure the new depth of water and the depth of the sediment.
4. Repeat the measurements next lesson.

Collect
Cold and warm microscope slides
Microscope
Pipette
Salol

Igneous rocks
When molten salol cools it crystallises. Investigate the effect of speed of cooling on the appearance of the salol crystals.

1. What are rocks made from?
2. **Collect** and complete a rock cycle diagram.
3. Write a short report on each experiment. Remember to write a conclusion.

B Fossil fuels

Use any resources available to write a short report on how one fossil fuel is thought to form. Remember to write any information in your own words.
Choose from
- coal
- natural gas
- oil.

Visit a local builder or builders' merchant. Ask what rocks are used in local buildings.

4.3 Rock roadshow

A Roadstone

The top layer of a road is made up of pieces of rock bonded together by **bitumen**. However not every rock is suitable for road making. The road surface should
- be hard
- weather slowly
- prevent water from passing through it
- prevent cars from skidding.

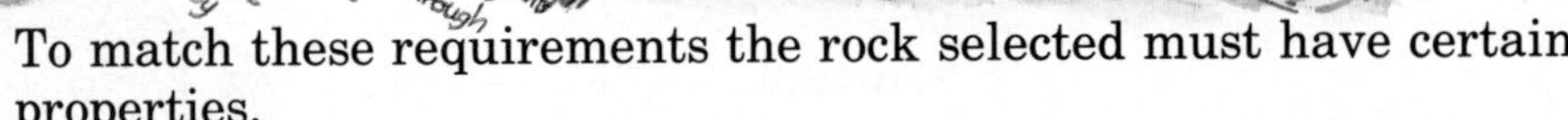

To match these requirements the rock selected must have certain properties.

a Most of the minerals in the rock should have a hardness greater than 5 on the **hardness scale**.
b The rock fragments must wear unevenly to make a skid-free surface. At least two different minerals of different hardness should be present.
c The rock fragments should have a rough surface for the bitumen to stick to.
d The rock must not let water through, nor shatter in cold weather.
e The rock should not be damaged by acid.

Collect

3 rock samples
Information card
Hand lens
Nail
Glass slide
Steel blade
Metal file
Bottle of acid
Dropper
Safety glasses

Investigate the properties of the 3 rock samples.

Make up a checklist for your tests.

Compare the rocks by
- using available information
- making observations
- designing and carrying out tests for properties **d** and **e** above
- estimating their hardness using the tests below.

Hardness scale

1 fingernail crushes

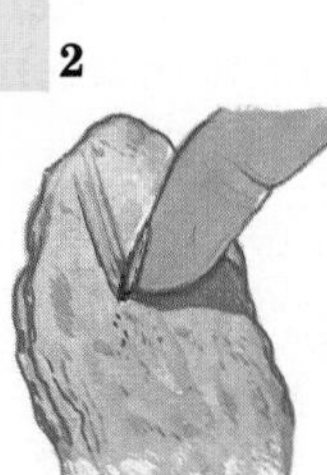

2 fingernail scratches

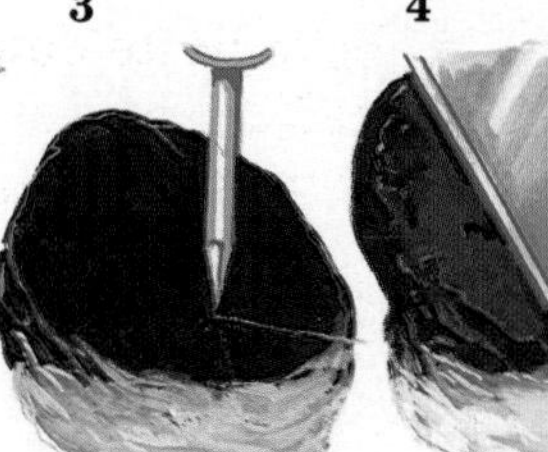

3 iron nail scratches

4 glass scratches

5 steel blade scratches

6 metal file scratches

Write a report of the investigation for the civil engineer in charge of building the road.
Describe the tests you did.
Recommend one of the rocks for the road's surface.

B More properties

The rocks and minerals shown are raw materials. These rocks are important to us because of their properties.

Coal . . .

for fuel

Sandstone . . .

for building

Important metals can be extracted from these minerals.

Malachite (contains copper) . . .

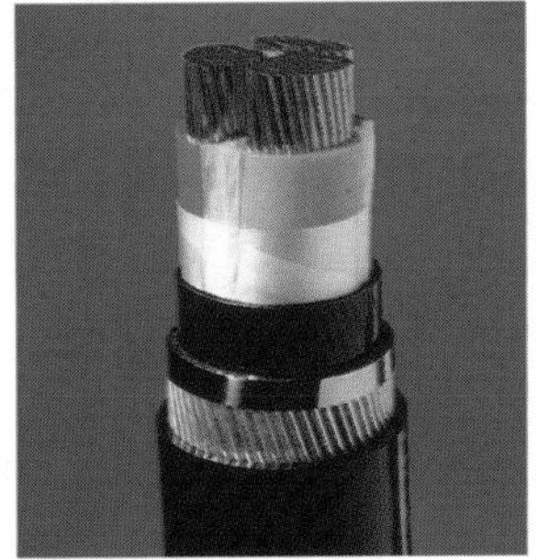

for electrical wiring

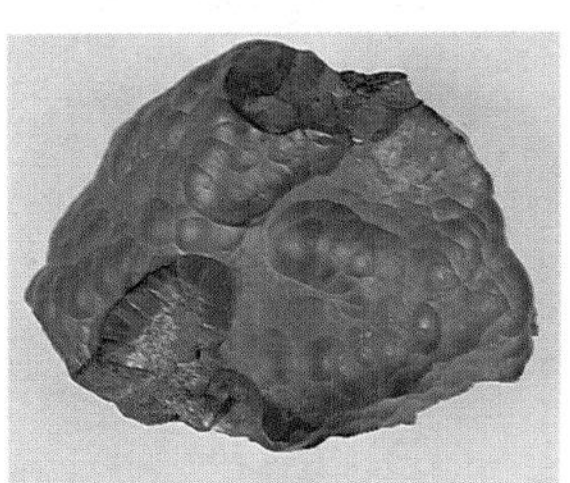

Haematite (contains iron) . . .

for construction

For each example above write down
- why they are useful raw materials
- the properties that make them useful raw materials.

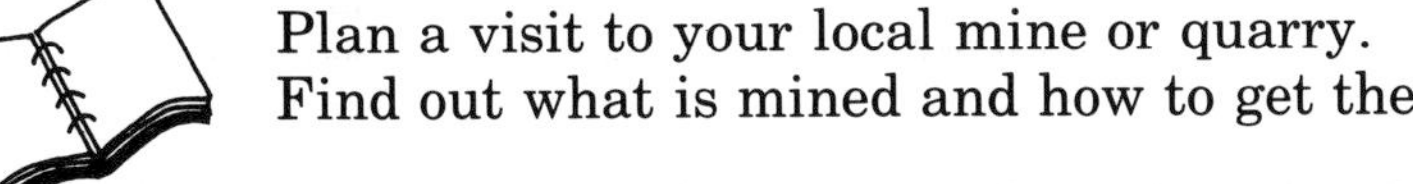

Plan a visit to your local mine or quarry.
Find out what is mined and how to get there.

Is there anybody out there?

Spacecraft that were launched in the 1970s and 1980s to study the planets have now left our solar system and are continuing to travel into outer space. They will take many thousands of years to reach the nearest stars. Each spacecraft carries a message from Earth to any intelligent life forms that might locate it. The plaque below is attached to the side of *Pioneer 10* launched in 1972. It was the first spaceship to leave our solar system, in 1989.

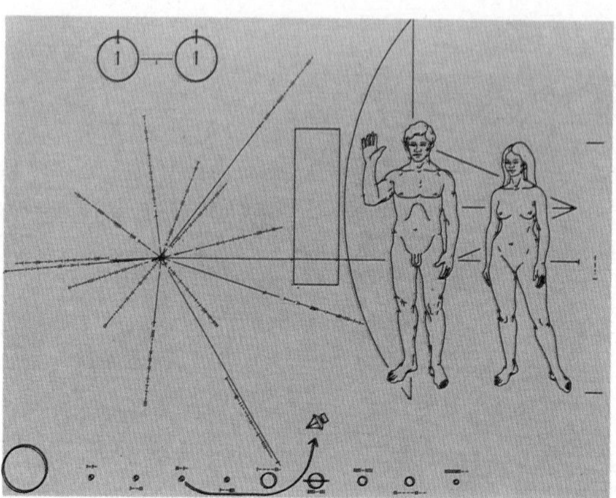

The Pioneer 10 plaque was carefully designed to show what kind of beings launched the spacecraft, from where, and when. The diagram on the left shows the Sun's position relative to 14 pulsars (stars emitting radio energy) and enables the time elapsed since the launch to be calculated

Collect

Poster paper
Coloured pencils
Tape recorder
Blank tape

Work in a small team.
Design and produce your own interstellar message to send into space. There must be 3 parts to your team's message:

- a plaque for the outside of the spacecraft
- a short tape of Earth sounds
- a set of 5 Earth objects.

1 Discuss why the images on the *Pioneer* plaque were chosen.
2 Design your own plaque on poster paper. Make a key for the images you have chosen to show.
3 Discuss what sounds should go on your audio tape. Record these.
4 Discuss what objects you would send. Collect these if you can.
5 Select the best ideas from the class. Assemble the whole 'interstellar message'.

1 Write a complete description of the interstellar message and explain why you have chosen each image, sound and object. Include a drawing of the plaque.
2 Bury the message in the school grounds – you never know what kind of living thing will dig it up in the future.

4.5 Talkabout

Rock history

How can these geological formations be explained?

What do they suggest about the history of the area?

What do you think they will look like in a million years from now?

a These Austrian mountains are far from the sea, yet their rocks contain fossils of tiny sea creatures

b A lava tube in Hawaii

c A sea stack in the Orkney Islands

d Folded rock layers near Lulworth in Dorset

e Part of the Grand Canyon in Arizona

A star's life

Astronomers think that a star is born when a huge cloud of gas, mainly hydrogen, is drawn together by gravity. As the volume of the gas cloud gets smaller the gas gets hotter and the pressure within the cloud increases. The atoms of hydrogen at its centre or **core** collide more often. When hydrogen atoms collide hard enough they combine to form helium. This reaction releases energy and the new star shines. Eventually the outward pressure caused by the energy release inside the star balances the inward pull of gravity, and the star stops contracting. It settles down to steadily burn its supply of hydrogen fuel. The star has reached 'middle age'. For a star like our own Sun middle age lasts for about 10 thousand million years.

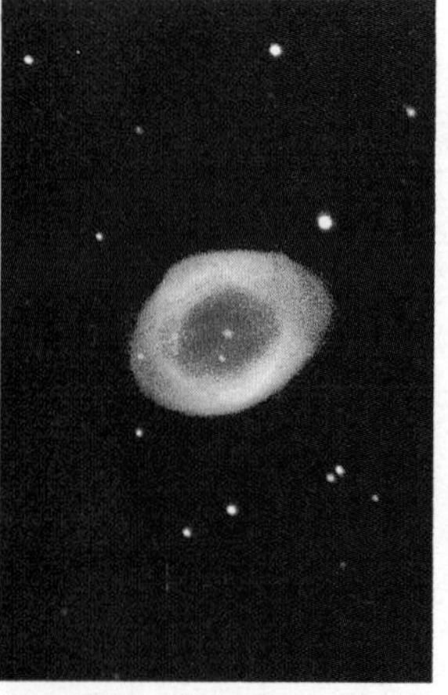

The Ring Nebula, a shell of gas remaining from a nova explosion about 20 000 years ago

When all the available hydrogen in the core has turned to helium, the star's middle age is over and it enters 'old age'. Gravity makes its core shrink and get even hotter, but its outer layers swell and cool. The star becomes a **red giant**. What happens next depends on the size of the star.

The core of a medium-sized star like our Sun contracts until collisions between helium atoms in it form atoms of carbon and oxygen. Eventually the helium fuel will also be used up. The star's core will contract again and the outer layers will blow away, perhaps in an explosion or **nova**, leaving the hot core as a **white dwarf**. The white dwarf will very slowly cool, grow faint and die.

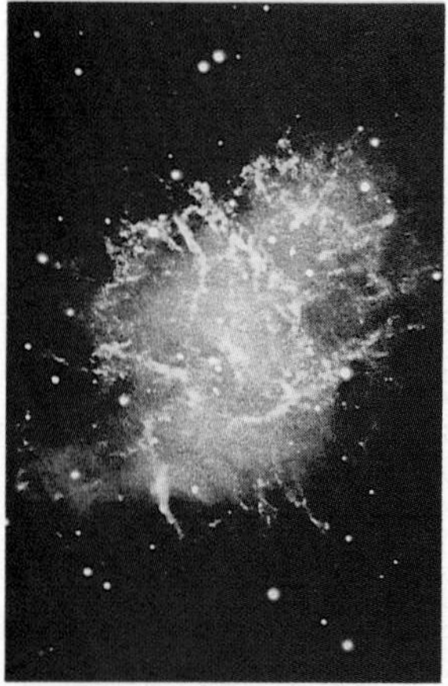

The Crab Nebula, the remnant of the 1054 supernova

The contraction in a larger star may lead to a much greater explosion called a **supernova**, which can shine as brightly as a whole galaxy. In 1054, a new light appeared in the sky that was bright enough to see during the day. It faded after two years, but the remains of this supernova can be seen today as a faint mass of expanding gas called the Crab Nebula. The very dense core left behind (a **neutron star**) spins rapidly and beams out radio waves like a lighthouse, and so is called a **pulsar**.

An even larger star may collapse further under the powerful gravity of its own mass to become a **black hole**. It will be very small and have a huge density. The gravitational pull of such a body is so great that even light cannot escape from it.

1 How do stars first form?
2 What fuel is used by a star when it is
 a in middle age **b** in old age?
3 When the volume of a gas decreases what happens to
 a the temperature **b** the pressure of the gas?
4 Draw a flow diagram to show the possible life histories of a star.

5

Energy on the move

Revision

5.0 Energy and forces

Energy

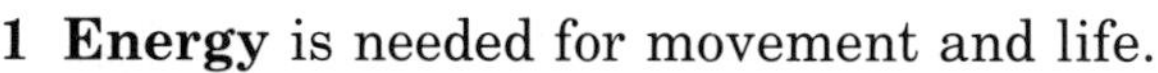

1 **Energy** is needed for movement and life.

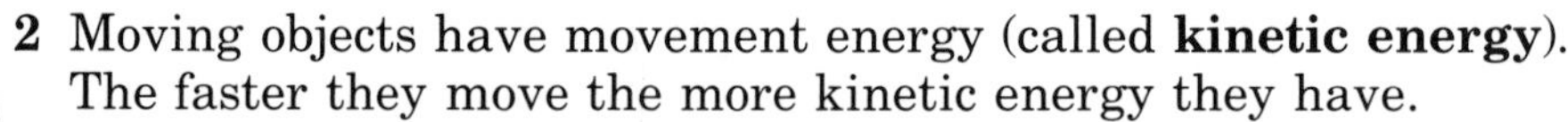

2 Moving objects have movement energy (called **kinetic energy**). The faster they move the more kinetic energy they have.

Using stored chemical energy

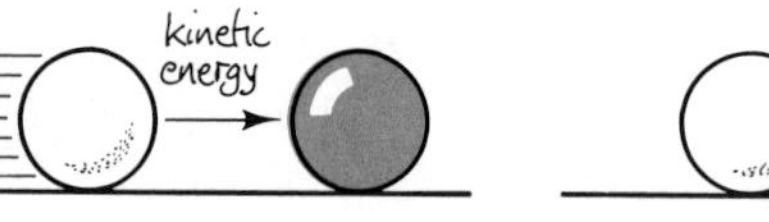

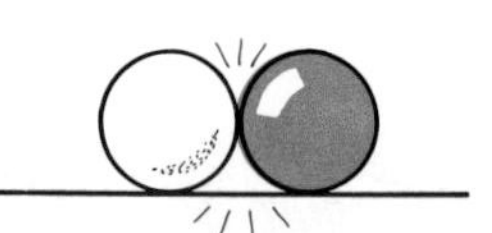

Passing on kinetic energy

3 Energy can be stored so that it is ready for use. Stored energy is called **potential energy**.

4 Energy stored in batteries, fuels, food and (non-nuclear) explosives is called **chemical energy**.

5 Electricity is an especially useful way of moving **energy** about. Electric current in wires carries **electrical energy** from generators or batteries where we can use it to do a wide range of jobs.

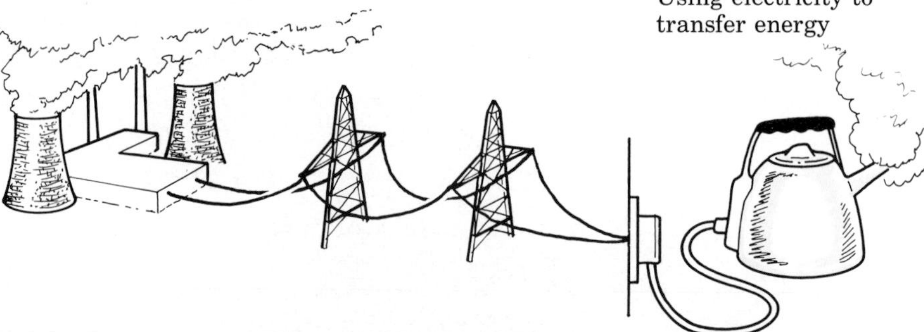

Using electricity to transfer energy

Forces

6 A **force** can push, pull, twist or tear. **Contact forces** act between objects that touch each other.

7 **Non-contact** forces can act between objects without them touching.

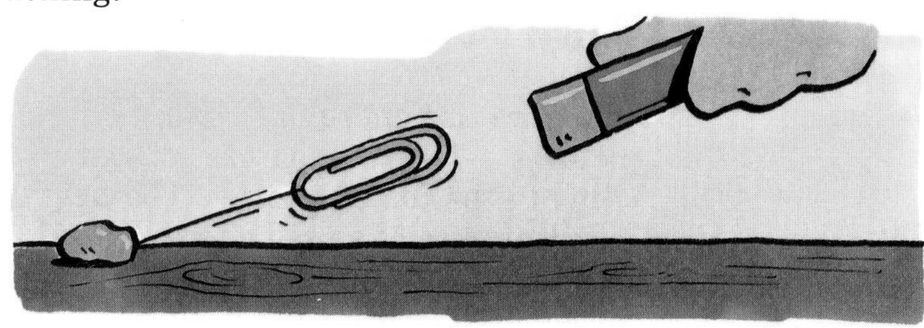

8 **Friction** is a force that acts against all movement. It is sometimes useful and sometimes a nuisance.

9 Forces can turn things and can be **balanced** by other forces.

1 You should know the meaning of the words in **bold**. If you cannot remember what a word means, look it up in a science book (like *Understanding Science 1* or *2*).

Collect and complete a revision question sheet.

2 **a** Copy and complete this table about energy.

Description	
the energy of moving things	
the energy stored by things that are high up	
the energy in wires from a battery	
the energy of springy things that are stretched or bent	
the energy of explosives and fuels	

b The pictures opposite and above show examples of types of forces. Give another example of each.

c Write an illustrated report on a toy that is powered by an 'engine'. In one part discuss the energy it uses and in another the forces that act and what they do.

CHECKPOINT

Find a dramatic picture for this Unit that illustrates 'Energy and Force'.

5.1 Using energy

A Energy changes

When we use energy, it changes from one type to another. In the pictures below the girl uses stored energy in her body (chemical) to climb to the top of a tower. The height she gains gives her a different type of stored energy (gravitational). She then swings down on a rope and changes the gravitational energy into movement (kinetic energy).

The main energy changes of this activity are:

chemical → gravitational → kinetic

However the girl gets hot when she climbs. The rope and the air also get slightly warm when she swings down. So some of the energy also changes into heat.

The energy changes can be shown by an energy arrow. The thickness of the arrow shows roughly how much energy changes into the different types.

Energy can be measured and the unit used to measure all types of energy is the **joule** (J).

Using stored energy

Collect

What you need for your activity

1 Design an activity which illustrates one of these energy arrows.

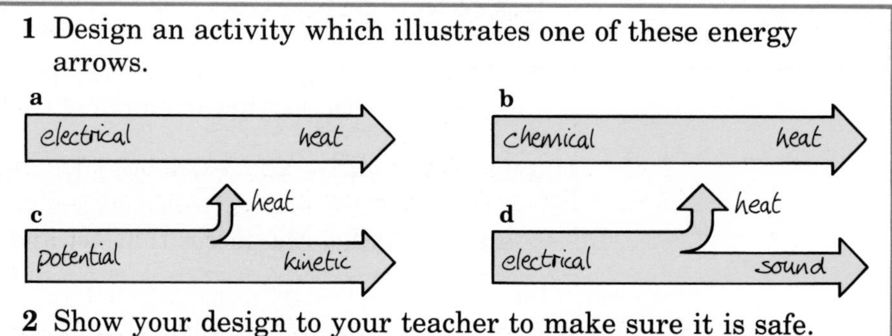

2 Show your design to your teacher to make sure it is safe.
3 Try out the activity.

1 Describe what you did.
2 Make a drawing of the energy changes that take place when you
   a clean your teeth
   b toast a slice of bread
   c make a tape recorder work
   d make water run out of a tap.
3 Choose one of your drawings and describe what has lost energy and what has gained energy.

B Energy chains

The girl swinging down on the rope is only part of an energy story.

- She got her gravitational energy by climbing up the ladder.
- The energy for this came from her muscles and from the chemical energy in the food she ate.
- The energy in the food came from sunlight.

So there is a chain of energy that goes back to the energy of sunlight.

The story also continues because the girl has kinetic energy that must change into another type. If, for example, she slides to a halt, the kinetic energy changes to heat energy which warms her shoes and the ground.

The complete energy chain therefore starts with sunlight and ends as heat. Nearly all energy chains start and finish this way.

Each picture shows the middle of an energy chain.

1 **Collect** a set of energy story cards
2 Sort the cards into the four stories (these three pictures and the girl opposite).
3 Put the cards into the correct order for each story, and write the story in your book.

Make up an energy story of your own.
Draw a picture for it and write out the story in steps.
Examples could be: flying a kite, climbing a mountain, burning a bonfire.

Collect packet labels from your kitchen that show the energy of foods.

5.2 Heat on the move

A Conduction and convection

Conduction

Heat is energy that moves from hot objects to cooler ones. There are three main ways that this can happen, one is **conduction**.

If you hold the handle of a teacup and stir the hot tea with a metal spoon which hand will get hot first?

Heat travels unseen through the spoon and rapidly reaches your fingers. The movement of heat energy through materials in this way is called conduction.

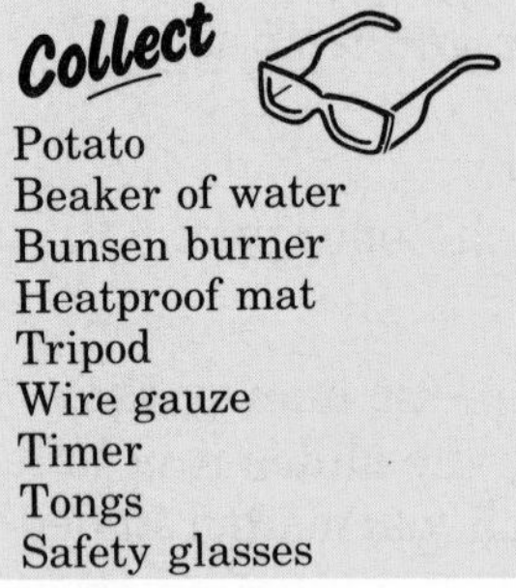

You can see (and measure) the conduction of heat through a potato in this experiment.

1 Put enough water in a beaker to cover a potato. Boil the water.
2 Put the potato in the water and let it boil for 3 minutes.
3 Carefully remove the potato and cut it in half. You will be able to see how far the heat has been conducted into the potato.
4 Make measurements and work out roughly how long it would take for your potato to cook right through.

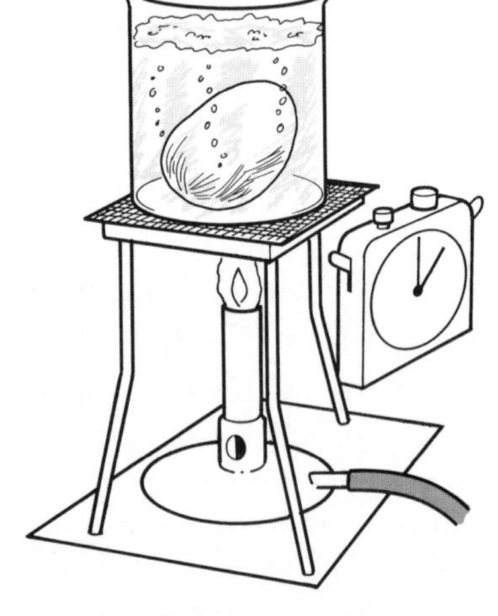

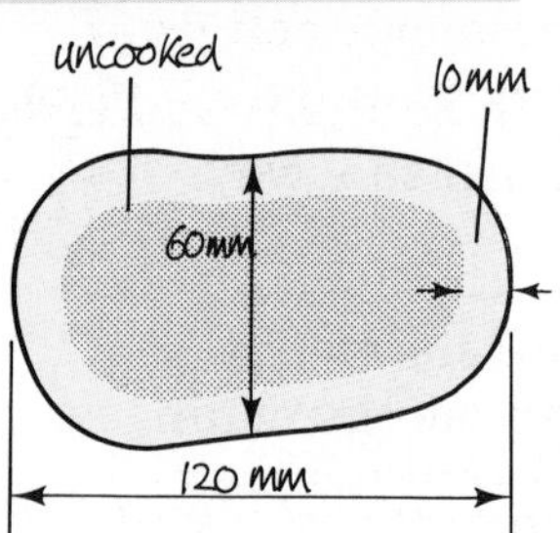

1 Write a report of your experiment, including your measurements.
2 The diagram shows a potato that has been cooked for 1 minute. How long would it take to cook right through?
3 Why do we often cut potatoes into smaller pieces when we cook them?
4 Estimate how long it takes the heat to reach your fingers through the spoon above. Does it travel faster or slower through the potato?

Convection

Another way of transmitting heat is by **convection**.

Heat can be carried upwards by rising currents of warm gas or liquid. Air expands when it is heated and becomes less dense. Cold air then sinks and forces warm air to rise. The moving currents of warm and cold air are called **convection currents**.

Collect

Round-bottomed flask
Clamp stand
Washing-up liquid
Spatula
Aluminium powder
Ice cube
Heating coil and power supply
Candle

Fill the flask with water. Add two drops of washing-up liquid and a pinch of aluminium dust. **Take care not to breathe in the dust.** Gently shake the flask and then allow the water to settle. The dust will show up any convection currents in the water.

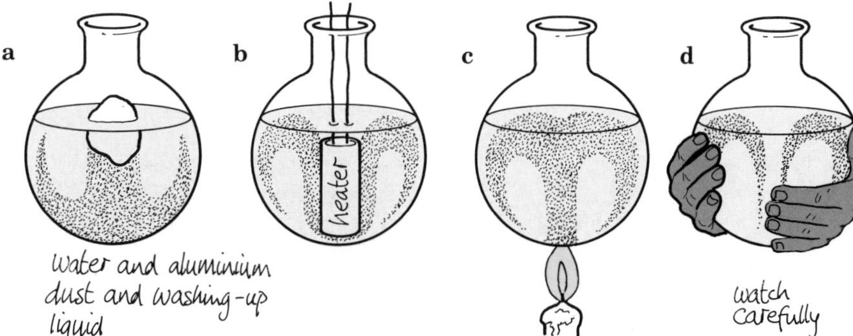

a Lower an ice cube into the water.
b Hang the heating coil in the water.
c Stand a lighted candle below the flask.
d Hold your hands against each side of the flask.

Watch closely. Draw diagrams of any convection currents you see in your flask.

1 Write a report of your observations from these four activities.
2 What is your explanation of what you have seen and felt?
3 Can there be convection currents in solids?

CHECKPOINT

B Heat watch

Look at the everyday situations below. Make a table to describe them as conduction or convection. Add some other examples of your own.

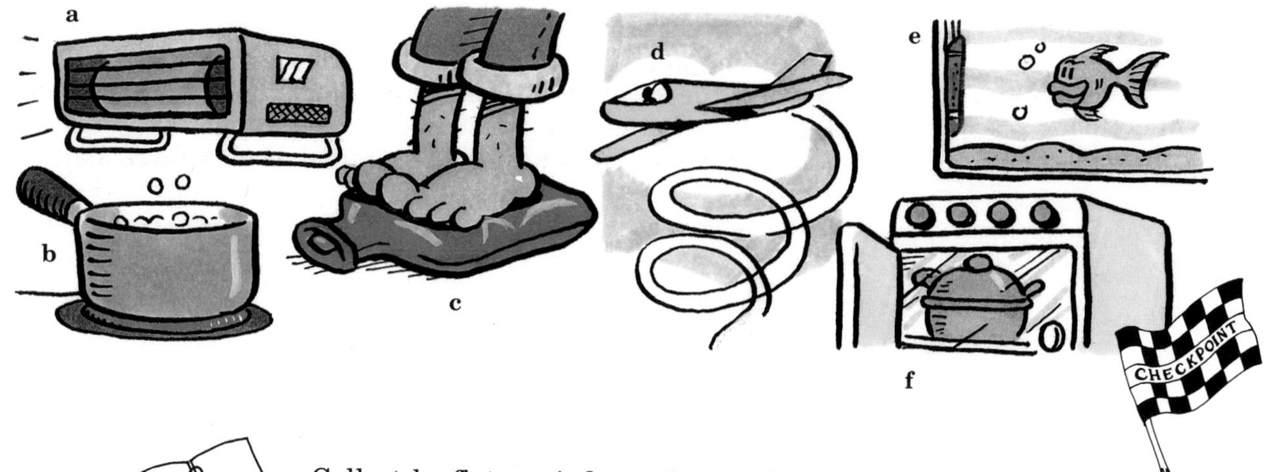

Collect leaflets or information on duvets from a local store.

5.3 Heat radiation

A Energy through space

Not much heat reaches the old man in the picture by convection, because convection currents carry heat upwards. Nor does it reach him by conduction because air is a bad conductor of heat. And yet heat *does* reach him from the fire.

The hot fire sends out heat waves, or heat **radiation** (also called **infrared** radiation) that give him their energy when they pass into his skin and clothes.

The heat energy received on Earth from the Sun reaches us by radiation.

Is it better to be a dark-coloured animal if you want to warm up quickly in the sunshine, or is a light-coloured skin better?

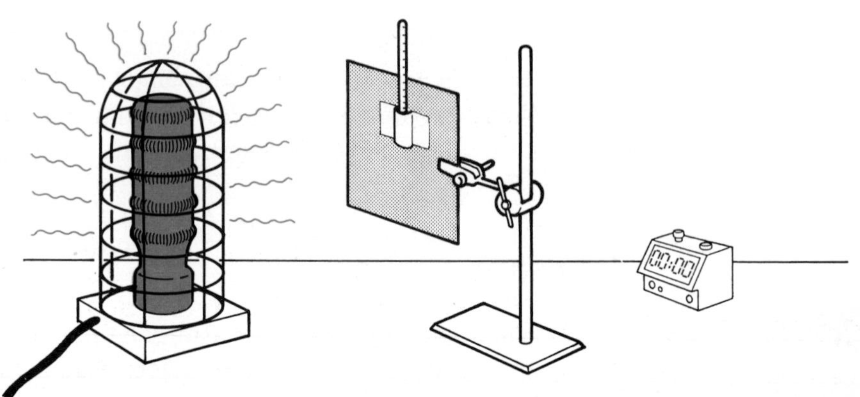

1 Switch on a radiant heater and let it warm up.
2 Put a thermometer in the slot of the copper sheet. Support the sheet on a stand. (It is your 'pretend' animal!)
3 Push the sheet close to the heater and start timing.
4 Measure the temperature of the 'animal' each minute as it heats up.
5 Remove the heater and measure the temperature as it cools.
6 Repeat with the other surface facing the heater.

Collect

Radiant heater
Copper sheet
Thermometer
Timer

1 Present your results in a neat table.
2 Plot two graphs of your results on the same temperature/time axes.
3 a What kind of skin would help the animal to warm up quickly in the sunshine?
  b Name three animals that have this skin type.

CHECKPOINT

B Heatwaves

This picture gives more information about the properties of heat radiation.

Electric fires and light bulbs use heaters that glow red or white hot and give off lots of heat radiation.
Make and test an electric heater.

1 Wind 1 metre of Nichrome resistance wire on a glass rod to make a neat coil.
2 Join the ends of the coil to stiff copper leads using connecting blocks.
3 Put your heater into water in a beaker and connect it to a 12 V power supply.
4 Obtain readings of temperature every minute as the water warms up.
5 Think of ways of improving your heater. Check the ideas with your teacher and try them if they are safe.

Nichrome wire
Glass rod
Connectors
Copper leads
Screwdriver
Beaker
Thermometer
Timer
Power supply

1 Make a list of the properties of heat radiation.
2 Write a report on your home-made heater and how you improved it.
3 Make a list of appliances that contain electric heating elements.
Put a * against those that get red- or white-hot and give out large amounts of heat radiation.

CHECKPOINT

Obtain information on the ‘protection factors’ of sun-tan creams.

5.4 Speed

A Friction-free motion

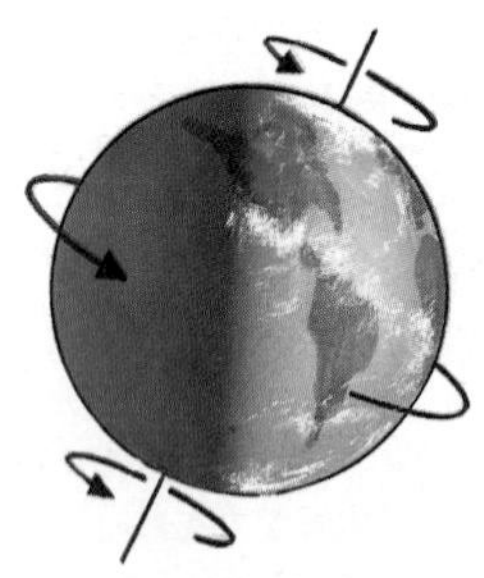
'Perpetual' motion

The Earth has been spinning ever since it was formed thousands of millions of years ago. It does not need a force to keep it going because there is very little friction in space to stop it.
On the Earth, friction acts against anything that move, so a force is needed to keep things moving.

1 Try these ways of making (almost) friction-free motion.

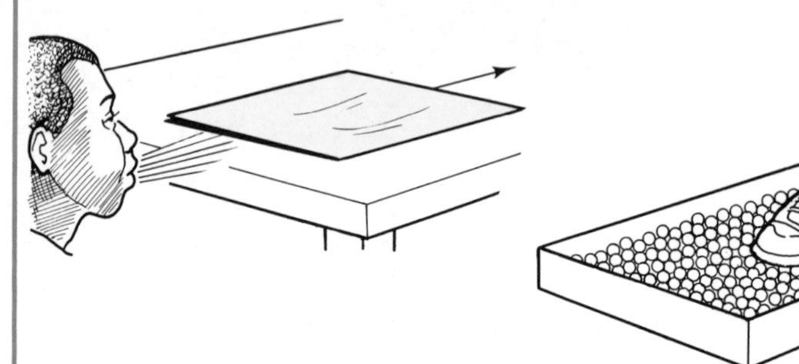

Collect
Sheet of paper
Beads in a tray

- **a** Blow gently under a sheet of paper that is lying on a table.
- **b** Put a handful of polystyrene beads in a tray. Put a shoe on the beads and test how freely it moves.
- **c** Does a banana skin really reduce friction between a shoe and the ground? Investigate and design a way of finding out.

2 Your teacher may show you a model hovercraft.
Measure how far it can travel when there is very little friction.

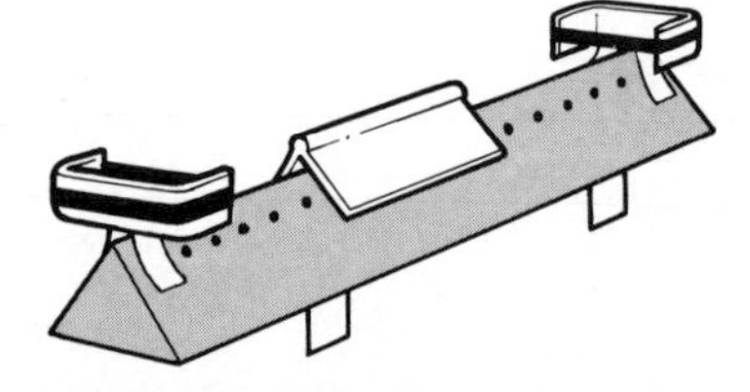

1 Write a report on your attempts to make friction-free motion.
2 The cartoon shows a brave rocket-powered skater on perfectly smooth ice.
She gives her rocket a 2-second burst of power. How will this make her move? How could she then stop herself?

B Whizz-bang-wallop

We use forces to get ourselves moving and forces to bring us to a stop. Force from our legs on the pedals of a bike accelerates us away from traffic lights. Forces between the brake blocks and the wheels bring us screeching to a stop. The more force we use, the faster we accelerate and brake.

Collect

Tape-measure
Chalk
Bike
Crash helmet

Use this test to measure the braking distance of a bicycle.
Work with a partner.

a Find a safe straight track.
b Draw a chalk mark across the track.
c Shout 'stop' when your partner crosses the line as a signal to apply the brakes.
d Measure the braking distance.
e Wet the brake-blocks and try again.

Do the test at three speeds; slow, medium and fast.
Take great care not to brake so hard that you fly over the handlebars.

Write a report on your findings.
Present your results in an interesting way that is easy to understand.

Find information on road speed limits in this and other countries.

5.5 Shaping up to force

A Force distorts

Think of what force can do to some of the things in your kitchen cupboard. With the force of your fingers you can
- make a dent in butter
- snap a biscuit
- stretch jelly
- bend a piece of spaghetti
- break off a piece of cheese.

Forces can change the shape of materials by bending, stretching and twisting them.

Collect

Spaghetti
Drawing pins
Thread
Ruler
Graph paper
Glue gun and heatproof board or sticky tape
Newton spring balance
Masses

1 Spaghetti bend-o-meter

a Design a way of measuring how much you can bend a stick of spaghetti before it breaks.

b Use your invention to find out if all spaghetti sticks bend by the same amount before they break.

2 Spaghetti is a difficult material to work with. It is brittle and breaks rather easily. You can however make it stronger by joining sticks together into a framework.

a Build a spaghetti framework to support a shoe above the bench. You will be charged an **imaginary** £1 per stick. The best framework will be the strongest one that contains the least spaghetti.

b Test your framework to destruction. Measure the greatest weight it can support.

1 Describe your spaghetti bend-o-meter and list the results you obtained. Make a bar chart of your results.
2 Draw a picture of your spaghetti shoe support. Say how much it 'cost' to build and how much weight it could support. How could you have made it stronger?
3 Think of things from the kitchen to complete the table below.

Property	Item
Brittle – snaps easily	
Elastic – stretches and returns to its shape	
Plastic – stretches and does not return to its shape	
Strong – hard to stretch	

CHECKPOINT

B Feel the pressure

You cannot push your thumb into a table but with the same force you can push a drawing pin into the wood. To explain how the same force can have such different effects, we must consider the area on which the force presses. When the area is small, like the point of a drawing pin, the force makes a hole in the wood and we say it exerts a large pressure.

We can feel large pressures in other ways.

Collect
cm-squared paper
Newton balance

Find out who in your class makes the greatest pressure on the ground and who makes the least.
Before you start guess who these people might be. The pressure depends on their weight and the area of their feet.

1 Draw round your shoes on cm-squared paper.
2 Count the squares to get the area of contact (only count part-squares if they are more than half).
3 Measure your weight.
4 Calculate your pressure from

$$\text{pressure} = \frac{\text{weight}}{\text{shoe area}}$$

5 Add your result to the class list.

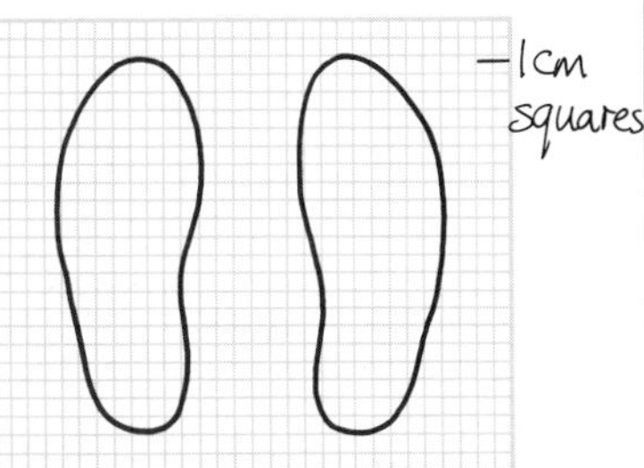

1 Write a report that includes your original guesses and the names of the actual people with the greatest and least pressure.
2 Collect results from the class and put them into a table (use a computer spreadsheet and program it to do the calculations for you).

CHECKPOINT

Cut out pictures of different types of bridges.

5.6 Be more forceful

A Turn up the force

Some tools we use are designed to increase our turning force. Door knobs, handlebars, food whisks and spanners are examples. They use a lever or wheel to turn a small axle with greater force.

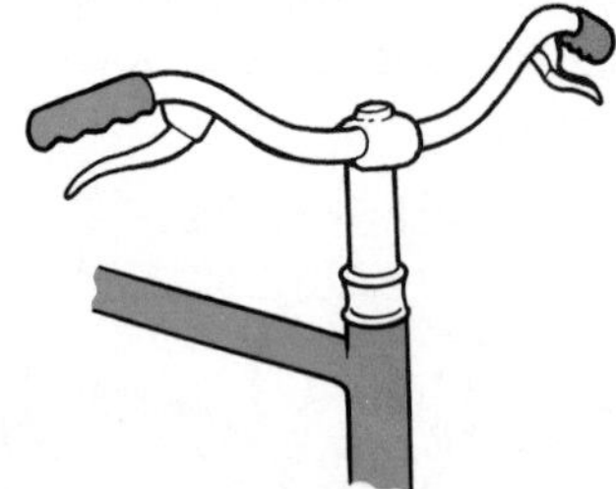

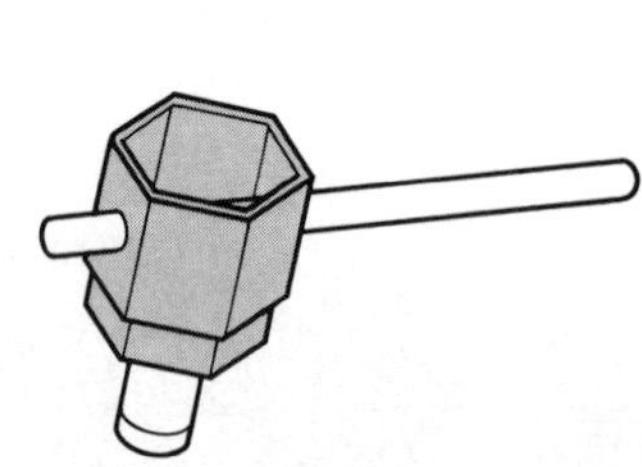

Collect

3 clamp stands
Bosses
Clamps
2 broom handles or rods
String

Find out which of these machines can lift a bag with the least force.

1 Build each machine as safely as you can. Make sure it is well engineered and runs smoothly.
2 Test each machine with the same bag and find out which one • uses least force • lifts fastest.

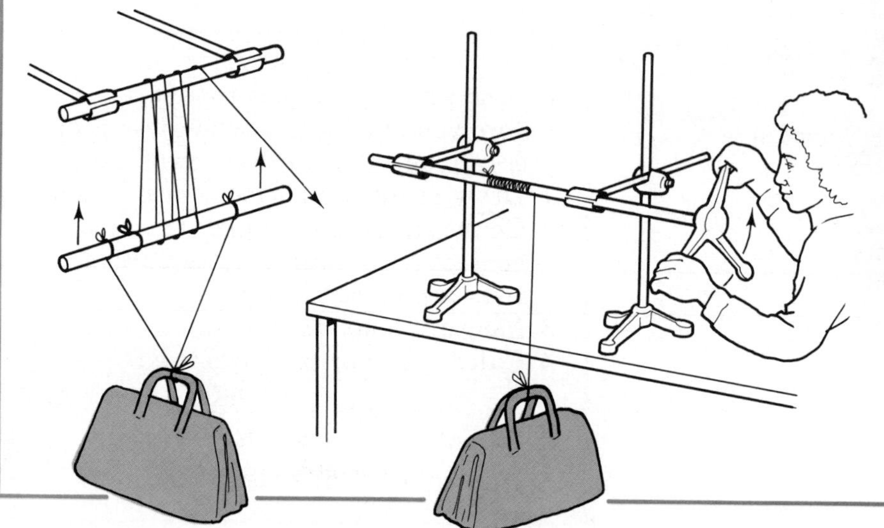

1 Draw a picture of each of your machines.
2 Say which machine lifts the fastest and which uses the least force.
3 How could the force needed to lift the bag be reduced further?
4 Think of a machine for increasing turning force that is not shown in the picture above. Describe how it works.

B Bicycle power

The bicycle is a wonderful machine. It is used as a means of transport all over the world. It is one of the most energy-efficient ways of travelling. It uses far less energy to make a journey than a petrol-driven machine. It is rivalled only by birds in flight. It even beats walking. Cycling takes about the same energy as walking but gets you there three times faster, so it uses only about one third of the energy for a given journey. Not only that, it is less tiring because you sit down and your muscles do not have to support your body. It is pollution free (apart from your 'exhaust' gases) and does not use fossil fuels.

The bicycle is a strange machine because it does not increase force. It is designed to multiply distance. The bike moves forward further than our feet do on the pedals, but we have to push harder with our feet than the wheels push on the ground.

Collect

Bicycle
Weights
Measuring tape
String

Do some measurements on your bicycle.

1 Support the bike upside down and put it into a chosen gear.
   - **a** For one turn of the pedals, find out how many times the back wheel goes round.
   - **b** Find out how the force on the pedals compares with the force on the wheel (hang weights on the wheel and the pedal so that they balance). Is the force on the pedal greater than on the wheel?

2 Repeat for other gears if you have time.

Write a scientific report on the advantages of a bicycle. Include results from your investigation. Present them in a way that is easy to understand.

CHECKPOINT

Obtain a brochure of a bike you would like to own.

5.7 Talkabout

The greenhouse effect

Some gases in the Earth's atmosphere act like the glass of a greenhouse. They let in the Sun's shorter-wavelength light and infrared (heat) energy, which warm the Earth up. However, they do not let out some of the longer-wavelength infrared energy that the Earth radiates back towards space. If it were not for this 'greenhouse effect' the Earth would be very much colder than it is.

Methane, water vapour and some other naturally occurring gases contribute to the greenhouse effect. So do some new artificial gases like CFCs, but the main 'greenhouse gas' is carbon dioxide (CO_2).

Humans and all other animals breathe out CO_2, and it is also produced in large quantities when fuels are burned. Trees, other plants and algae absorb CO_2, but not as fast as it is now being produced, so the amount of CO_2 in the atmosphere is slowly but steadily increasing. This may be strengthening the greenhouse effect and so causing the average temperature of the Earth to rise, a problem called 'global warming'.

The amount of CO_2 in the atmosphere is increasing. CO_2 traps the Sun's heat like a greenhouse. Earth's average temperature will probably rise by at least 2°C in the next 40 years.

Industrial countries burn coal to make electricity. This produces large amounts of CO_2.

Nuclear power stations make electricity without producing CO_2, but are expensive and dangerous.

Hydroelectric dams, wind, waves, tides and geothermal energy can also make electricity, but not yet on a very large scale.

Higher temperatures will dry out summer vegetation quicker, resulting in more fires.

Weather will generally become more extreme, with more blizzards and droughts.

Most modern transport – cars, planes, etc – burns fuels made from oil, producing more CO_2.

Some cooler places will warm up enough to grow new and better crops.

Coastal cities and even whole countries may be flooded by rising sea levels.

Other places will become too hot and dry for the crops now grown there.

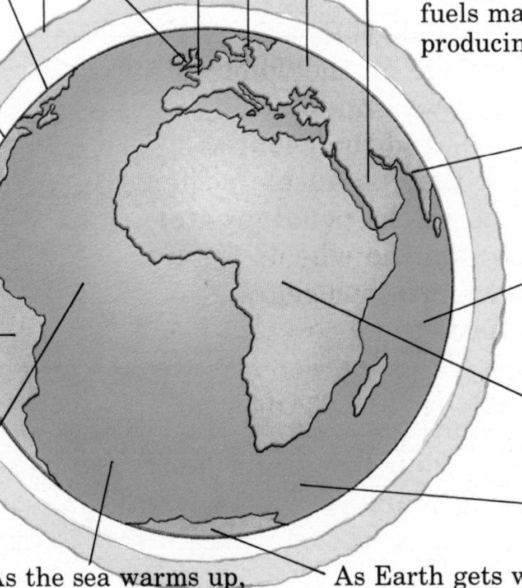

Algae in the sea absorb much CO_2, but pollution is killing them.

Trees absorb CO_2 as they grow, but forests are being cleared to give land for farming.

Poorer countries want to raise their living standards – as richer countries have done – by burning more fuels and making more electricity.

Wood is burned as fuel in poorer countries, releasing more CO_2.

Ocean currents may change, causing local climate changes and movements of fish stocks.

Sea levels will probably rise by at least 30 cm in the next 40 years, mainly because water expands as it gets warmer.

As the sea warms up, storms and hurricanes will become more frequent.

As Earth gets warmer, more snow and rain will fall on the poles and on high ground.

Global warming would not make everywhere on Earth hotter. Probably some places would warm up more than the average while others would actually get colder. Some would also get wetter and others drier. Where these different changes would occur and what all the results would be is a very complicated question, that scientists cannot yet answer.

Some possible results of global warming, such as more frequent hurricanes, are undesirable while others, like cool areas being warmed up enough to grow abundant crops, may be beneficial. A single result could even help some people at the same time as harming others. For example, fish might shift to new feeding grounds, giving some fishing fleets better catches and others poorer ones.

Crops in some areas may be improved by global warming effects

Global warming may make hurricanes more frequent

Fish may move to new feeding grounds

Work in groups of three.

1 **Collect** a copy of the diagram and ring the comments that mention
  a the causes of global warming
  b the effect on sea level and climate
  c the results for crop growing and fishing.
  Use a different colour for each of **a, b** and **c.**

2 Choose one of **a, b** or **c** and note down all the comments that relate to it. Speak about it to the rest of the group. If you can, add further reasons and comments.

You should not think only of your own point of view. Consider the interests of people from different parts of the world, such as Brazilian farmers, car drivers in California, fishermen from Pacific islands such as Tuvalu or bakers in Siberia.

Forested areas in Brazil are cleared to provide more land for crops and pasture

No pressure at all!

The ancient Greek philosophers did not believe that there could be such a thing as 'nothing' or emptiness. We call nothing a vacuum. Most Greek philosophers would have thought the whole idea of a vacuum silly. They even had some experimental evidence for their view. They wrote that a bellows simply would not open if it had been pushed flat and air was not allowed in. 'Just close the end of the tube from the bellows and try to open it. If you could it would be full of nothing. But you can't, can you? This is because you cannot have a space full of nothing. Our theory predicts that it is nonsense to say something is full of nothing.'

The Greeks were not far wrong in their experiment. Try it yourself with a syringe instead of bellows. You can't fill it up when your finger is over the end. Is this because it is impossible to have a vacuum?

Most scientists of the ancient world agreed that air was certainly something, that it had weight and that a vacuum could not exist. There were just a few thinkers with different ideas. They said that air was made up of tiny particles which rushed about. If the particles were the air what was in between them? These 'Atomists', as they were called, thought that there was nothing at all between them. Air was particles moving about in a vacuum.

Galileo Galilei

Galileo Galilei (1564–1642) was a famous Italian scientist who spent much of his life observing nature and doing experiments to test his ideas. He is most famous for improving the telescope and for his observations of the Sun, Moon and planets. These supported the theory that the Sun is the centre of the solar system and not the Earth.

He was also interested in whether air had weight and whether it was possible to have a vacuum. As always Galileo thought carefully, and did not accept unquestioningly what the ancient Greeks had thought. He did his own experiments to test his theories. He had weighed air by pumping it into a flask fitted with a valve. The flask weighed more 'full' than 'empty'. So he knew the weight of air.

Evangelista Torricelli

Just before he died Galileo, who had become blind in 1637, invited a brilliant young mathematician called Evangelista Torricelli (1608–47) to work with him. One of the experiments they planned together was to investigate the strange space that appears above water in a very long tube. They thought it might be a vacuum. At that time the idea of making a completely empty space was as exciting as a 'black hole' is to us now. Indeed many people argued that a vacuum would be black, like looking into an empty hole or out into the night sky.

A group of five or six scientists carried out the experiment (unfortunately Galileo had died). First they got hold of a very long lead tube. Then they had a thick glass flask sealed into it at the top. They fixed the whole thing to the side of a tower of a house which had a convenient staircase and windows. The bottom end of the tube was in a tub of water on the ground and the rest roped to the tower.

First of all someone closed a tap at the bottom of the tube. Then the scientists went to the top of the tower and filled up the tube and flask to the very top with water. The idea was to close the flask and open the tap at the bottom to see if the water would fall and leave a vacuum in the flask. They were so eager to screw down the top of the flask tightly that they overdid it and broke the tube. So they all had to go home and wait for another piece of apparatus to be made.

Later the scientists gathered again and fixed up the 36-foot (about 11-metre) high tube and flask. This time they were more careful and it worked just as they had predicted. The water fell a little and then stayed at a level of 34 feet. It left what looked like air at the top of the flask - or was it a vacuum?

The scientists stared at the space. Now the problem was just what Galileo had said it would be. How could you recognise a vacuum?

1 Do you believe in the existence of a vacuum?
What would you do to try and prove it?
2 Draw and label the experiment that the scientists carried out.
3 What could the Italian scientists have done to show that they had made a vacuum?

High pressure energy

It takes a lot of energy to blow up a balloon. Some of this is stored in the compressed air and the stretched rubber. When air is forced into a smaller space, its pressure rises and it gains energy. This energy can be got back by releasing the air and making it do work. Air compressors can be seen in garages or being used by workmen on the roads. A pump fills a tank with compressed air that is then used to work pneumatic drills and tools.

1 Build a machine that works by compressed air. The pictures show two examples (and an instruction sheet is available), but invent a machine of your own if you can.

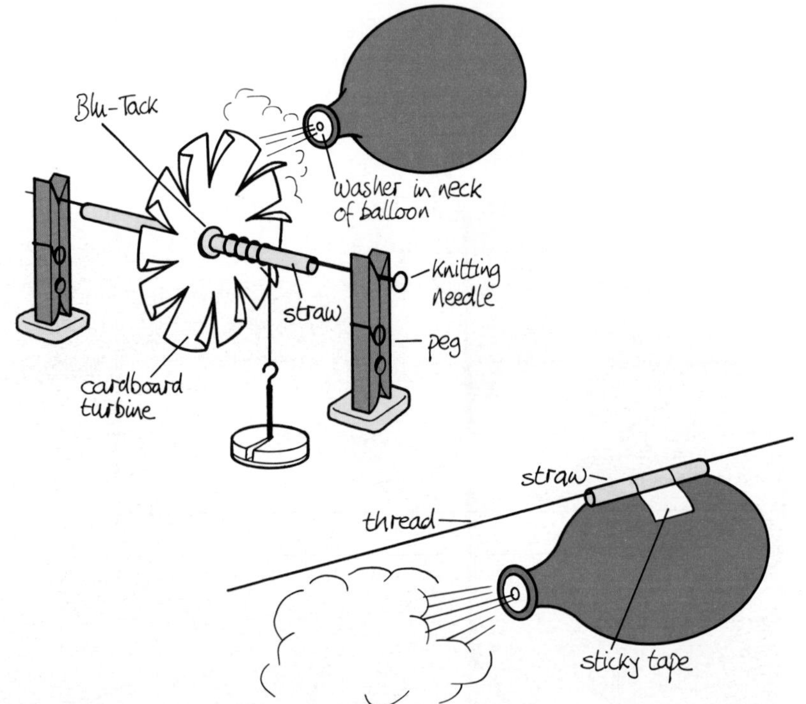

2 Enter your machine into a 'class competition' and explain its good points. A panel of judges could decide which is the class winner.

1 Report on the energy changes that take place in your machine.
2 You can make compressed air by closing your mouth and blowing out your cheeks. List three ways of using this compressed air. Say what happens to the energy in each case.
3 Compress some air in a bike pump. Compare the force you need to push in the handle half-way with the force needed to push it three-quarters of the way in. Report on your findings.

6

Ideas of substance

Revision

6.0 Substances

1 Everything is made from **elements**. There are 92 natural elements and about 15 other artificial elements. Most elements are metals. The elements are arranged in the **periodic table**.

2 A **compound** is made when two or more elements are joined together.

3 A **mixture** is made when substances mix up but do not join. There are several ways of separating mixtures, for example

4 Elements in a compound can only be separated if **energy** is used. For example, heat can break some compounds up, electricity can break others.

5 Some examples of common elements, compounds and mixtures are:

6 An important scientific **hypothesis** is that *all substances are made of particles.* For example an element is a substance that contains one kind of **atom**.

7 Some substances are made of **particles** called **molecules**, each of which is made by joining two or more atoms together.

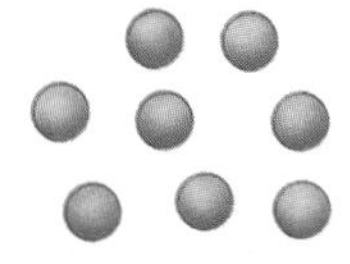

Atoms in an element

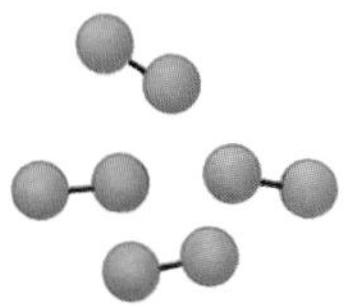

Molecules in an element

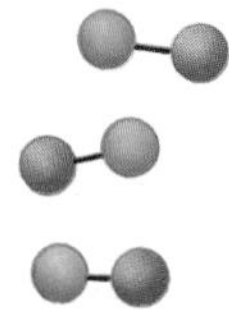

Molecules in a compound

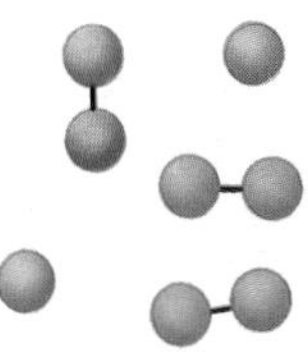

A mixture of 3 elements

8 Substances can be changed into other substances. This change is called a **chemical reaction**. It often involves a transfer of energy to or from the surroundings.

9 A **word equation** can help to describe a chemical reaction. For example:

hydrogen + oxygen → water.

1 You should know the meaning of the words in **bold**. If you cannot remember what a word means, then look it up in a science book (like *Understanding Science 1* or *2*).

Collect and complete a revision question sheet.

2 New substances can be made by chemical reactions. Imagine that you could discover three new substances, each one helping to make the world a better place (for you or for others). Describe the properties that you would want each substance to have and give each one an appropriate name.

CHECKPOINT

Find the names of four substances used for DIY work in the home. Collect an advertising leaflet for one if you can.

6.1 Chemical reactions

A Everyday reactions

When bread burns it joins with oxygen in the air and changes into new substances. Once the bread is burning, heat energy is given out into the surrounding air. This is an example of a chemical reaction. It can be described by a word equation.

bread + oxygen → burnt bread + gases

Substances on this side are called the **reactants**	Substances on this side are called the **products**

Chemical reactions are happening all the time; near you, on you and even in you. The following processes are all chemical reactions.

Name of reactant(s)	Name of reaction	Description of product(s)
1 bread + oxygen 2 petrol + oxygen	*combustion*	burnt bread + gases exhaust gases
3 acid in stomach + tablets 4 acid soil + lime	*neutralisation*	neutral solution neutral soil
5 car + oxygen 6 silver ring + oxygen	*corrosion*	rusty pile of junk tarnished surface
7 iron ore + carbon 8 copper ore + carbon	*metal extraction*	iron metal + slag + CO_2 copper metal + slag + CO_2
9 salt water 10 molten salt	*electrolysis*	sodium hydroxide + chlorine sodium metal + chlorine gas

In each case the product of the reaction is a new substance. It has **different** properties from the reactants.

In most cases, when energy is transferred to or from the surroundings, you can see or feel or measure the change.

Collect

Dry boiling tube of oxygen
Iron powder
Copper powder
Zinc powder
Burning spoon
Bunsen burner and heatproof mat
Safety glasses

1 Your teacher will show you how to fill a dry boiling tube with oxygen.
2 Wear safety glasses. React each metal powder in turn with oxygen gas as shown. Look for any sign of an energy change.

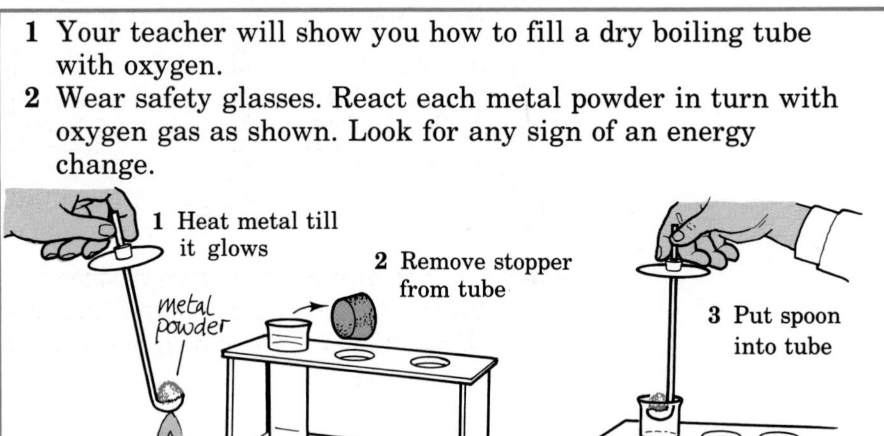

> 3 Examine the metal oxide which has formed. Find some evidence that it is a different substance from the metal that you began with.

1 Choose one of the metals.
Write about the energy change and the change in appearance during the reaction with oxygen.
2 The reaction of zinc and oxygen can be shown as a word equation.

zinc + oxygen → zinc oxide

Write similar word equations for your other reactions.
3 Which metal was most reactive with oxygen?
Explain why you picked this metal.
4 Put the metals in order of reactivity, the most reactive first.

B Active reactions

In a chemical reaction
- a **new substance** is formed and it can sometimes be observed
- an **energy change** occurs and it can sometimes be observed.

> All the activities which follow involve a chemical reaction.
> For each activity
> - write a suitable title
> - list any evidence of a chemical reaction.
>
> 1 Watch your teacher demonstrate this . . .
>
> 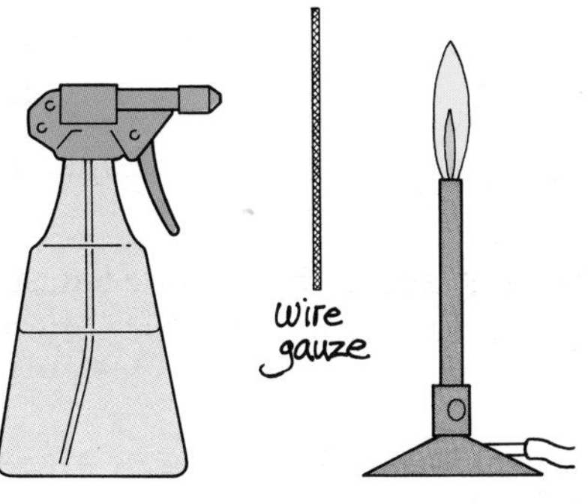
>
>
> 2 and this . . .
>
> 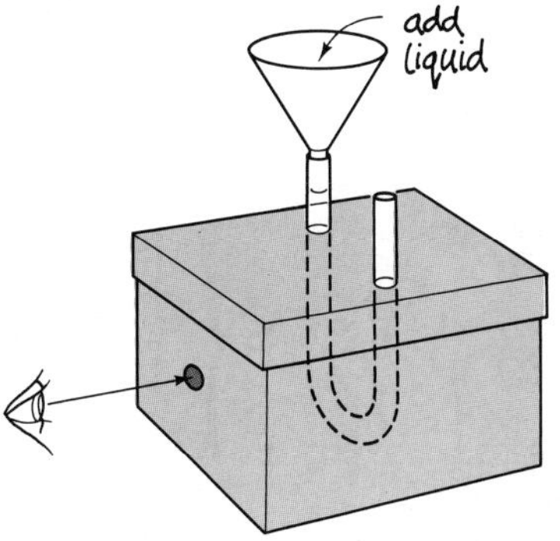
>
>
> **3–8** Collect **one** of the activity boxes.
> Follow the instructions and then return the box.
> Write your report and then do another activity.

Take a photograph or make a drawing of some local examples of metal corrosion.

6.2 Speeding up reactions

A Kitchen chemistry

Some reactions happen quickly, others slowly.

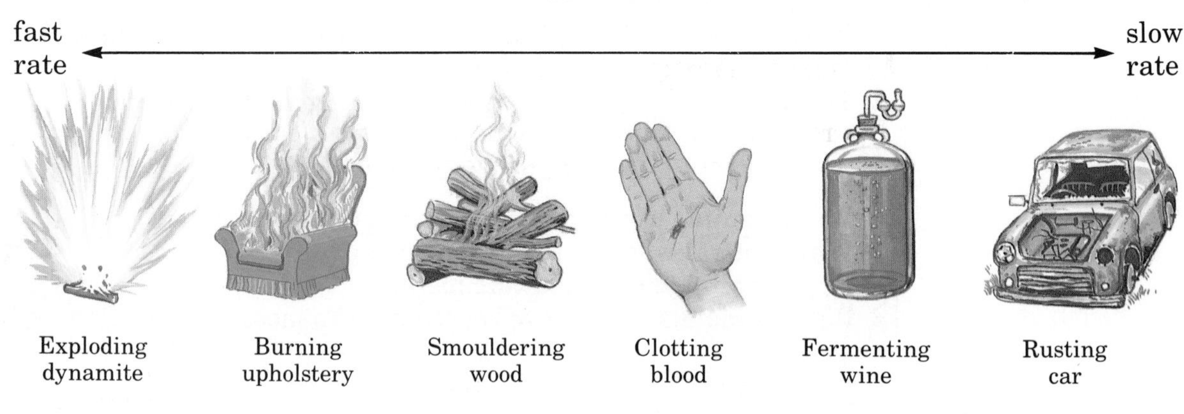

Exploding dynamite | Burning upholstery | Smouldering wood | Clotting blood | Fermenting wine | Rusting car

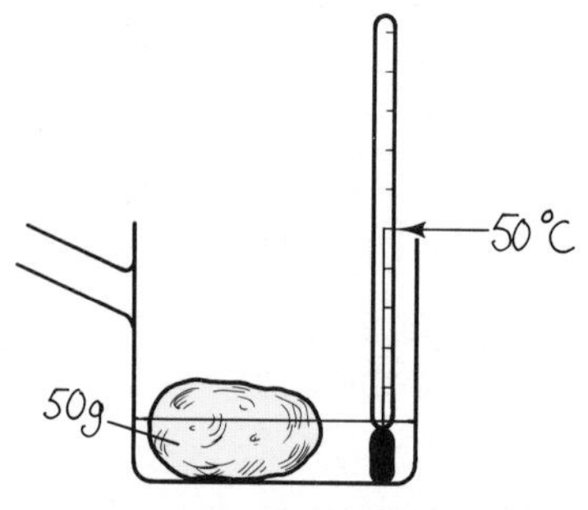

To cook a potato slowly

Sometimes you may want to change the rate of a reaction. For example, in the kitchen the rate of cooking can be speeded up. This is done in a number of ways.

Try to spot three variables that have been changed in the pictures to speed up the cooking process. You are going to investigate these variables **on your own.**

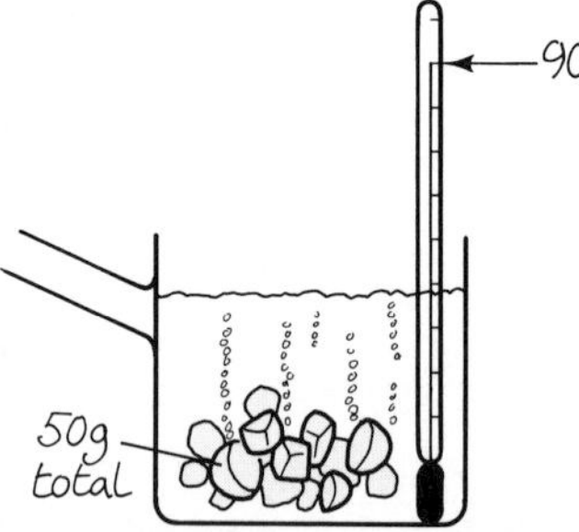

To cook a potato quickly

Collect

About 15 pieces of macaroni
Bunsen burner and heatproof mat
Anything else you need

Macaroni can be cooked using a Bunsen burner and some water. Plan your own individual investigation to test the hypothesis that each of the three variables in the picture above affects the cooking time of macaroni.
You should only change **one** variable at a time. Can you think why?

1 You will have to decide
- **a** which variable to investigate first; (*variable*)
- **b** how to control the other variables for a fair comparison; (*control*)
- **c** how to tell when the piece of macaroni is cooked; (*measurement*).

2 Write an outline of your plan in your book. Include a diagram.

3 Carry out your investigation.

4 Present your results in a suitable written form (table, chart, graph etc.).
(Ask your teacher for help if you are not sure what to do.)

1 What parts of your investigation went well? Why?
2 What parts did not go well?
3 Is there anything you would do differently if you started again?

B Using chips

The rate of most reactions can be changed. In this reaction marble chips react with acid. One of the products is a gas which bubbles into the atmosphere.

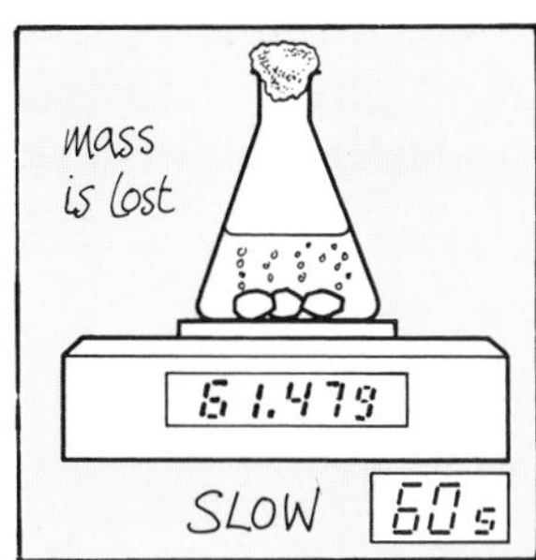

marble + acid → carbon dioxide + a solution

The faster the reaction, the more quickly carbon dioxide is produced. So a faster reaction loses mass more quickly.

Dilute hydrochloric acid
Marble chips
Conical flask
Measuring cylinder
Anything else you need
Safety glasses

You are going to investigate three variables which change the speed of this reaction.
Things to think about are *variable, control, measurements.*
You may use an accurate electronic balance for these experiments (the balance may be connected to a computer).
Take **great care** to follow the teacher's instructions because this equipment is expensive.

Use 20 cm^3 of acid in a conical flask for each experiment and with the balance find out if

a 5 g of *big* marble chips react faster than 5 g of *little* chips
b 5 g of big marble chips react faster in *warm* or *cold* acid
c 5 g of big marble chips react faster in the acid from the *bottle* or in *dilute* (watered-down) acid.

Write a report about **one** of the variables you investigated. Mention how you tried to make the experiments fair.

Obtain three cooking recipes. Use a highlighting pen to show any step in the recipes that will speed up the cooking process.

6.3 Catalysts

A Speeding things up

Reactions can be speeded up by increasing
- the temperature
- the surface area of the reactant(s)
- the concentration of the reactant(s).

Reactions can also be speeded up by using catalysts. A **catalyst** changes or **catalyses** the rate of reaction and yet it remains chemically unchanged at the end of the reaction. Catalysts are used in industry to control the speed of reactions and so cut down the cost of producing a new chemical.

The manufacture of ammonium nitrate for fertilisers is aided by . . .

. . . the use of a platinum catalyst to speed up ammonia production

$20\ cm^3$ of hydrogen peroxide solution
2 small beakers
Manganese dioxide powder
Bunsen burner and heatproof mat
Safety glasses

Collect

Zinc granules
Copper coin
Bottle of dilute hydrochloric acid
Anything else you need

1 a Gently heat the hydrogen peroxide solution in a beaker.
  b Divide the solution equally between the two beakers.
  c Add a pinch of manganese dioxide to **one** beaker and observe.

2 One granule of zinc will react with $10\ cm^3$ of acid.
  A few drops of detergent can be used to show the speed of the reaction.
  Design and carry out an experiment to find out if copper is a catalyst for this reaction.
  Things to think about are
  - which **variable** to change
  - how to set up an experiment and a **control** to compare it with
  - what **measurements** to make to indicate the rate of reaction.

1 Write a report about the two experiments. Include diagrams where they are useful in explaining your methods.
2 Look up and write down the meaning of the word *catalyst.* Do the results of your experiments agree with this meaning? Explain your answer.
3 If you have time, use the reference books available in class to find three reactions that are speeded up by catalysts. Write the name of each catalyst and describe the reaction that it catalyses.

CHECKPOINT

B Preservatives

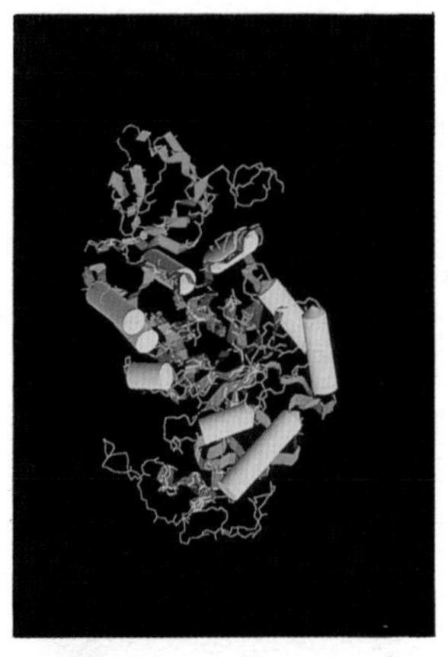

Computer graphic of the enzyme amylase, which breaks down starch

Living things also contain catalysts called enzymes. An **enzyme** controls a chemical reaction in a living thing. The chemical reactions in any living thing need catalysts – otherwise most of them would happen much too slowly to keep it alive. Your own body has thousands of enzymes, each one acting as a special tool to speed up, or sometimes slow down, one type of reaction.

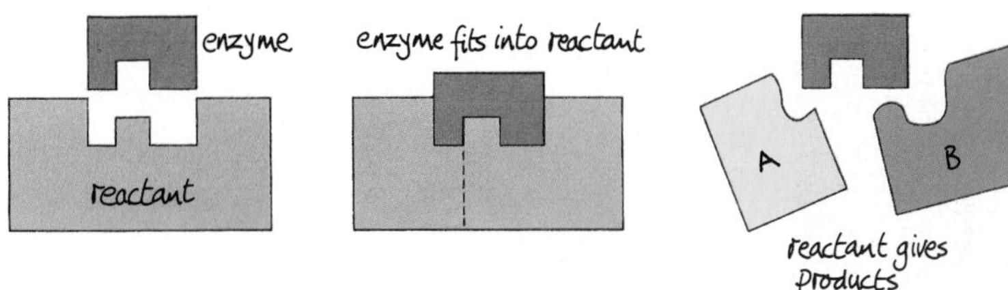

Enzymes are used to make foods like cheese, yogurt and vinegar (see *Understanding Science 2*, topic 6.4). Enzymes are also sometimes involved when food goes 'off'. For example, a damaged apple produces an enzyme that causes the tissue to react with the oxygen in the air and turn brown. This reaction (called **oxidation**) can be stopped by destroying the enzyme with heat or by using chemicals that slow it down. Such chemicals **preserve** the food.

Collect
Apple
4 test solutions

Find out which of the solutions prevents or slows down the browning of a piece of the apple. You will have to decide which **variable** to change, how to **control** the other variables to make any comparison fair and how to **measure** browning.

1 a Write a report about your apple investigation, making clear what you found out.

b What were the weaknesses of your investigation?
(*Hints*: Think about the accuracy of any **measurements** and whether there were any variables that you couldn't **control**.)

2 a Foods often contain preservatives (described by code numbers E200–E299) and anti-oxidants (E300–E399). What job does each type of additive do?

b **Collect** two food labels and a reference list of food additives. List the E numbers of the preservatives and/or anti-oxidants in each food. Find out and record the names of the chemical substances that have these E numbers.

CHECKPOINT

Visit or write to a local garage to obtain information about the catalyst that can be used in a car exhaust system.

6.4 Patterns in reactivity

A Metal reactions

The metal elements are similar in appearance; most are shiny and solid at room temperature. However metals do not all react in the same way. In topic 6.1A you discovered that zinc reacts faster with oxygen than iron which in turn reacts faster than copper. Other common metals can be burned in oxygen and the reactions compared.

Metals react with oxygen in the following order of reactivity.

Potassium metal burning in oxygen

Metal	Reaction	
Sodium Lithium Calcium Magnesium Aluminium	These metals burn well in oxygen A lot of energy is given out The metal glows brightly Metal oxide forms	**Most reactive**
Zinc Iron Tin Lead Copper Mercury	These metals burn less well in oxygen Energy is given out The metal glows slightly Metal oxide forms	↓
Silver Gold	No obvious reaction with oxygen	**Least reactive**

Bottles of:
Magnesium
Aluminium
Zinc
Iron
Tin
Copper
Dilute acid
Anything else you need
Safety glasses

Your task is to investigate this reactivity series using the metals from magnesium to copper in the series. Find out if the same pattern is observed when the metals are reacted with dilute acid.

Hints:
- use a small amount of each metal each time
- decide in advance how many metals to test
- decide which **variables** to **control** for a fair comparison
- decide how to **measure** the reactivity.

1 Explain what is meant by an *order of reactivity*.
2 Write a report about your investigation.
3 Would your investigation have been better if you had used more metals? Explain your answer.
4 Describe how you would improve your investigation if you had more time.

B Groups of elements

The two metals at the top of the reactivity series you have investigated are similar, so similar that they are considered to be part of the same 'family' of elements. This family is **group 1** of the periodic table and is called the **alkali metals**. Your teacher may show you some of their unusual properties. All elements in the periodic table are arranged in **groups**. The elements in each group have similar chemical properties. The diagram shows these groups.

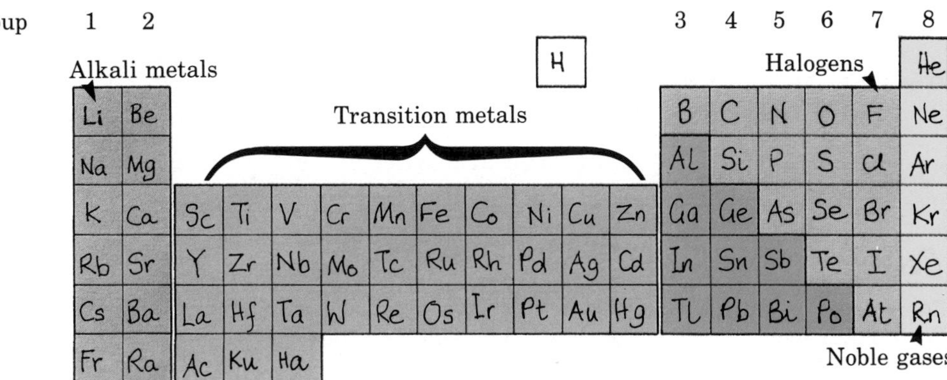

You are going to work as part of a group! – a team of people with a similar research task. Your task is to find out as much as you can about one of the following groups of elements:

- group 1 – *the alkali metals* • group 7 – *the halogens*
- group 8 (also called group 0) – *the noble gases.*

You can make use of any of the following (your teacher will tell you what is available):

a classroom textbooks **b** wall posters
c the knowledge of members of staff (you will only be able to interview each person for 2 minutes so prepare your questions carefully) **d** a computer database.

For your chosen group of elements:

1 Give the family name and explain why these elements are all in the same group of the periodic table.
2 Write a paragraph about your team's research. Include
   - the names of the group members
   - some of the family resemblances that you discovered
   - some of the uses of members of this family.

Cut out several adverts or articles (from magazines) which show or describe a metal.

6.5 Moving ions

A Electrolysis

Active metals are extracted (pulled out) from their compounds by using energy.

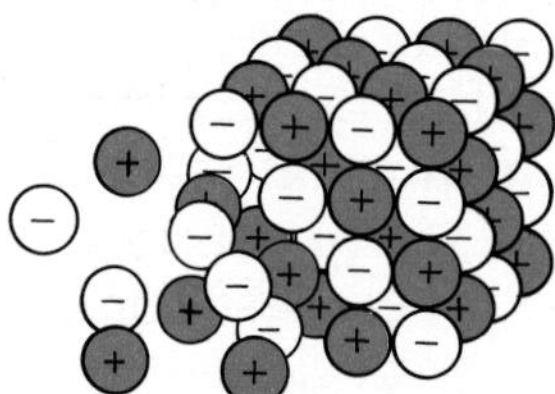

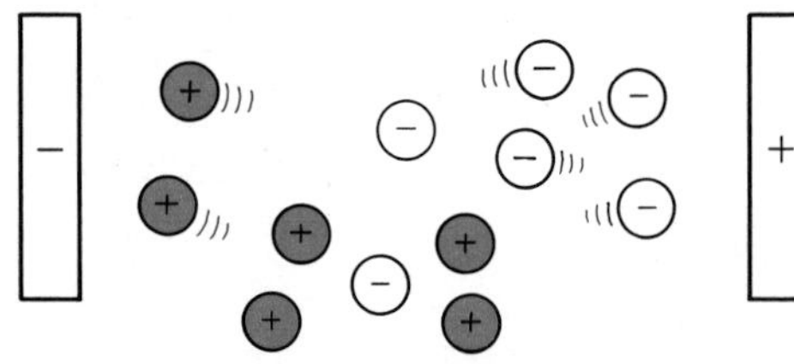

Heat or water separates the particles in the compound. The particles have an electrical charge and are called **ions**.

The electricity causes the ions to move. The ions form elements at the electrodes. The whole process is called **electrolysis**.

Collect

Filter paper
Potassium iodide solution
2 connecting leads
Crocodile clip
Power supply (8 V DC)

Collect

Solutions of:
Tin bromide
Zinc iodide
Copper chloride
Small beaker with 2 carbon rods
Another crocodile clip

Electrical writing

1 Set up this circuit.

2 Move the end of the free (red) lead over the surface of the filter paper and write your name.

Which way?

1 Set up this circuit.

2 Choose ONE of the solutions. Find out which electrode, +(red) or −(black), the metal ion moves to.

3 Choose another solution and again find out which electrode the metal moves to.

4 Write down a hypothesis about the movement of the metal ion and then use the third solution to check your ideas.

1 What do the words *ion* and *electrolysis* mean?

2 Draw a labelled diagram of one of your electrolysis experiments. Show clearly what evidence there was of a chemical reaction.

3 Is your hypothesis about the movement of the metal ion supported by your results?

4 A charged ion is always attracted to the electrode with the opposite charge. From your experimental results, what charge do you think

a a metal ion has? **b** a non-metal ion has?

Explain your answers.

B Coloured ions

Some ions are coloured. We can use this fact to show that ions move towards the oppositely charged electrode during electrolysis.

These solutions contain blue copper ions.

These solutions contain yellow chromate ions.

Copper sulphate solution

Copper ammonium sulphate solution

Potassium chromate solution

Sodium chromate solution

Collect

U-tube containing copper chromate solution in agar gel
Vinegar
2 carbon electrodes
Crocodile clips
Power supply (12 V DC)
Coloured pencils

1 Set up this experiment.

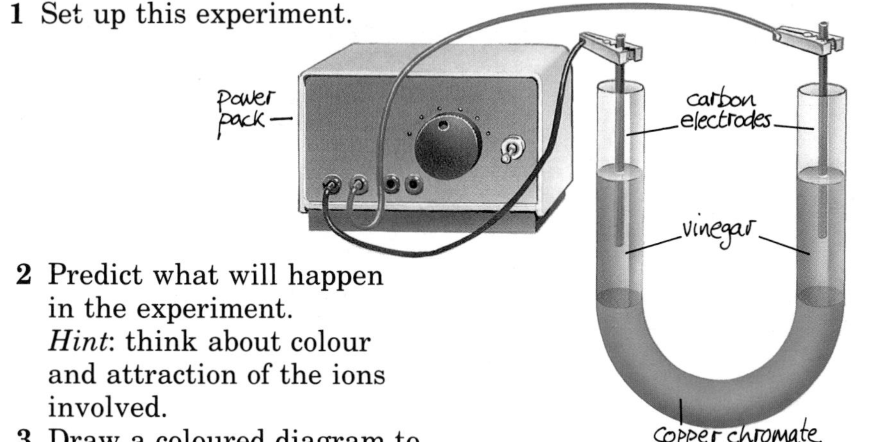

2 Predict what will happen in the experiment.
Hint: think about colour and attraction of the ions involved.
3 Draw a coloured diagram to show the result that you expect.
4 Look at the result after 15 minutes.

1 Describe your experiment. Did your results support your prediction?
2 Write down a likely explanation for the result of the experiment. Compare your explanation with those of others in the class.

CHECKPOINT

Find out how aluminium is made. Photocopy some useful information (or make a short video film sequence) about the everyday uses of aluminium.

6.6 Problem

Trail blazer

Chemical reactions occur in real life. You can see evidence of chemicals and chemical reactions in and around your school. Your problem is to design and map out a *Chemistry trail.* This will be similar to a nature trail. However, it will teach people something about the reactions around them.

This is an example of a nature trail. Look at it carefully.

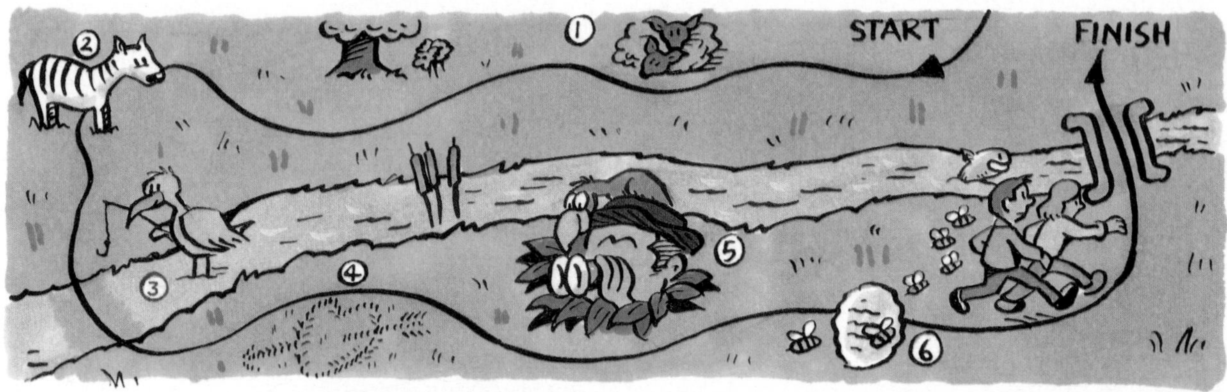

Now solve the problem

1 Decide which chemicals and chemical reactions will be good points of interest on your trail.

2 **Collect** a map of the school area and mark all the points of interest.

3 Make up and print a guide sheet (perhaps on a word processor) which describes each of the points of interest on the trail.

4 Test your trail on someone and change it if necessary.

Hints

1 Include examples of
- elements, mixtures and compounds in use
- unusual compounds that can be closely inspected
- corrosion
- reactions actually happening (look over this unit)
- catalysts in operation
- evidence of pollution.

2 Your methods could include
- asking questions to help people learn from the trail
- giving people something to do; for example, inspecting something with a hand lens or testing a liquid with pH paper.

3 Don't make the trail too long or too short; aim for a walk of about 15–20 minutes.

Radiation

Some substances are **radioactive**. This means that they contain unstable atoms that give out energy in the form of radiation. *Background radiation* is present all around us from natural sources like granite rock. People also try to design *good uses of radiation*. Great care has to be taken because *radiation can be harmful* if it is not controlled properly.

The phrases in *italics* are the titles of three talks. Your group will be given one title. The group has to plan and record a three minute talk about the **facts** behind the phrase. You can make use of any resources that you can think of. The panels below give you some hints.

Panel 1
How to give a talk

Panel 2
Background radiation

Panel 3
Good uses of radiation

Panel 4
Radiation can be harmful

6.8 Readabout

Atomic models

Elements

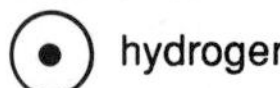

hydrogen
carbon
nitrogen (azote)
oxygen
sulphur
copper
phosphorus
lead

Compounds

water
ammonia
sulphuric acid

Dalton's atomic symbols

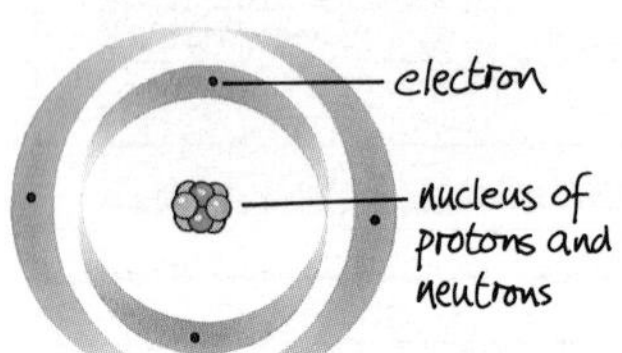

The nuclear model of the atom

Scientific ideas can change, and they can also cause change. A good example is the theory of the atom. What do you think an atom is? What does it look like? Has it got a colour or shape? Does it spin and wobble? What is it made of? Before you read on, draw, colour and label a picture of an atom to show how *you* imagine it.

An idea like 'the atom' takes many people and many years to develop. Around 400BC, Greek philosophers suggested that the world was composed of lumps of material, each too small to see, swirling around in total emptiness. These 'atoms' were thought to be completely solid, impossible to cut up and always on the move. Your own drawing of an atom may be very like this ancient idea.

Indian thinkers around the tenth century AD suggested that each of four elements had their own indestructable atoms. These invisible atoms were thought to cause effects that people could see.

Our modern theory of the atom is built on experiments conducted since the seventeenth century by several important thinkers. For example, John Dalton (1766–1844) was largely responsible for the idea that atoms are rearranged during chemical reactions to form new substances. He developed symbols to illustrate this.

By the nineteenth century Dalton's solid billiard-ball type of atom was largely accepted. However, experiments conducted by many people in many different countries during the twentieth century have changed the theory again. By 1940 the international model of the atom could be represented like the drawing on the left.

This is the nuclear atom. The idea that an atom is made of even smaller bits (called 'subatomic particles') is very important. Nuclear energy and nuclear bombs are direct results of the nuclear theory of the atom.

Scientists are still at work today on the theory of the atom. New subatomic particles like quarks and mesons have been discovered since 1940. It is certainly possible that a new revolutionary theory of the atom will cause great changes to the way *you* live.

1 Among the scientists who developed the nuclear model of the atom were Ernest Rutherford, Niels Bohr and James Chadwick. Find out some of the important things that **one** of these scientists did and write about your findings.
2 How has the 'nuclear atom' theory made our lives different from the lives of people who lived in the nineteenth century?
3 What is your opinion of nuclear power and nuclear weapons?
4 A person who has not made a final decision about something is said to have 'an open mind'. What is the value of keeping 'an open mind' about scientific ideas?

7

Smart ideas

Revision 7.0 Electricity and magnetism

1 A magnet can **attract**
- small pieces of iron (iron filings)
- other things made of iron or steel
- one end of another magnet – and it can **repel** the other end.

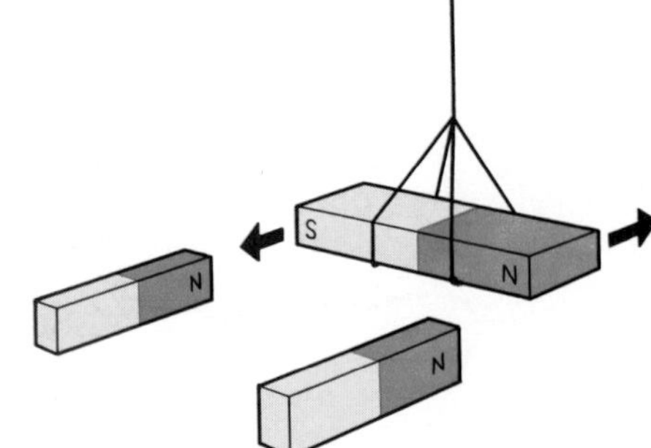

2 The **magnetic force** is a **non-contact force**. The magnet does not have to touch the objects for its force to act on them.

3 An **electromagnet** uses an **electric current** in a coil of wire to **magnetise** a piece of iron. The magnetism can be turned on or off by switching the current on or off.

An electromagnet

4 Pieces of plastic can be '**charged**' with electricity by rubbing them energetically with a cloth. A charged object has the power to pick up light objects such as pieces of paper, bubbles and feathers. The **electric force** is another non-contact force which acts through space and moves objects without touching them.

5 **Electronic circuits** make clever use of electric currents to do useful jobs for us. The currents are controlled by **components** and are given energy by **batteries** or '**mains**' **electricity**.

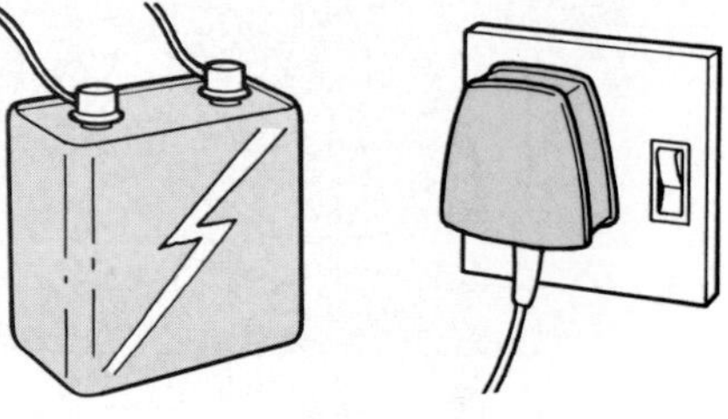

6 Examples of components in common use are
- switches
- resistors
- transistors
- integrated circuits
- sensors
- diodes.

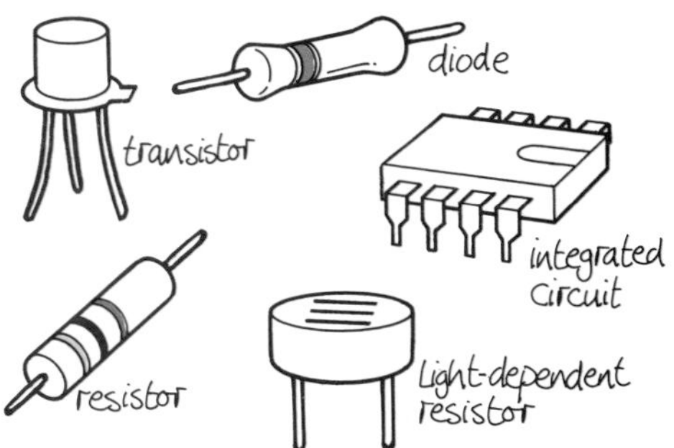

Electronic components

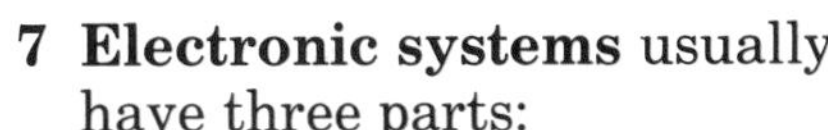

7 **Electronic systems** usually have three parts:

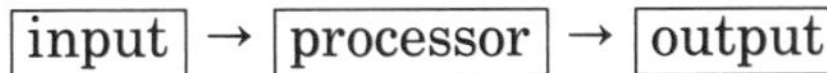

input → processor → output

An electronic system

1 You should know the meaning of the words in **bold**. If you cannot remember what a word means, look it up in a science book (like *Understanding Science 1* or *2*).

Collect and complete a revision question sheet.

2 **Make a compass**

a *Version 1*. Hang a strong magnet on a long piece of thread. Let it settle and one end of the magnet will show you magnetic North.

b *Version 2*. Magnetise a steel needle by stroking it with a magnet. Float the needle carefully on a saucer of water. Leave it to settle and one end will point North.

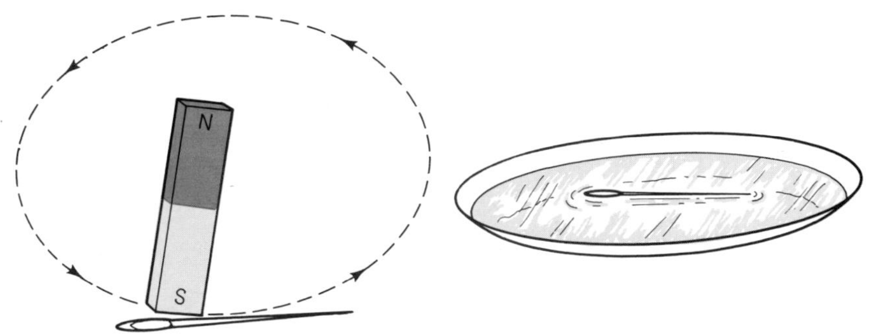

Draw a map of your home and street with North and South marked.

Electromagnetic machines

A Magnetic patterns

Magnets are surrounded by invisible **force fields** that reach out and exert forces on other magnetic objects. Currents in wires are also surrounded by these 'magnetic fields'. The Earth has a magnetic field that makes compass needles point to magnetic North. A sensitive way of revealing the pattern of a magnetic field is to use a small 'plotting' compass.

Collect

Plotting compass
Magnets
Paper

Investigate the pattern of the Earth's magnetic field in your laboratory and the patterns around magnets.

1 Lay a piece of paper in the magnetic field, choose a starting point and mark it with a pencil dot.
2 Put the tail of a plotting compass over this dot and draw a second dot at the point of the needle.
3 Move the compass along so that its tail covers this dot and continue.

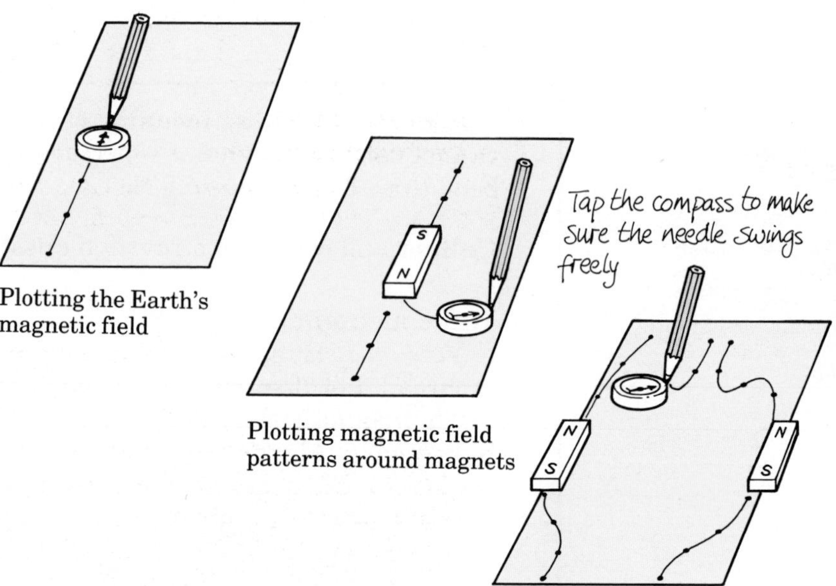

Plotting the Earth's magnetic field

Plotting magnetic field patterns around magnets

4 Dot the path of the compass needle as it leads you through the magnetic field. Then join up the dots to form a line.
5 Follow other lines by starting at different points until you have a pattern that shows the shape of the field.

1 Stick your pictures of magnetic fields into your book.
2 Find out and describe how you can use iron filings to show magnetic field patterns.

CHECKPOINT

B Electromagnets for inventors

Iron is a metal that can be made into a very strong magnet. A piece of iron can be magnetised by passing an electric current through a coil wound around it. The iron becomes a strong magnet when the current flows, but the magnetism disappears as soon as the current is switched off. This type of magnet is called an **electromagnet**.

Inventors have found many uses for magnets that can be switched on and off.

Collect

Compass
Insulated wire
Power supply

1 Investigate the effect of passing a current through a coil that is wound around a compass needle as shown.

a Wind the wire neatly round the compass.
b Line the coil up with the compass needle.
c Connect the coil to a battery or power supply.
d Experiment with the size of the current and/or the number of turns of the coil.

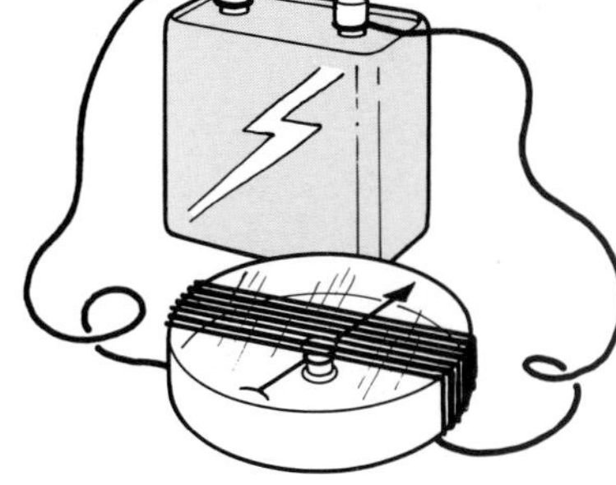

Collect

Steel key
Container of muddy water
Iron nail
Insulated wire
Power supply
Switch

2 **A problem to solve**
You have dropped a steel key into some muddy water at the bottom of a drain. Use the equipment in the *Collect* list to rescue the key.

1 Write a full report about the compass investigation.
2 Describe exactly how you rescued the key.
3 Invent another use for a strong magnet that can be switched on and off.

Obtain or copy a picture of the Earth's magnetic field as seen from space.

A An electromagnetic kick

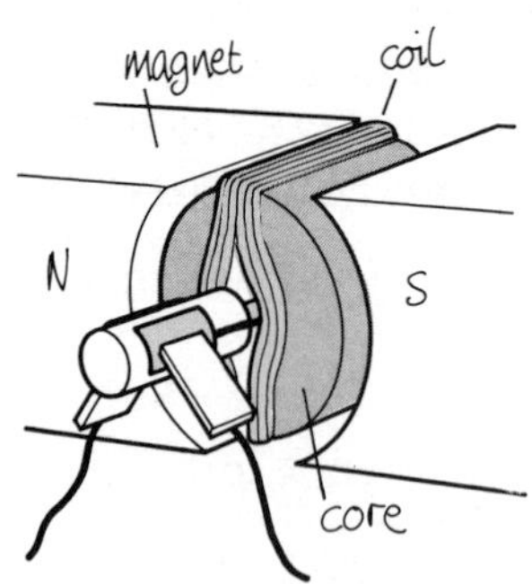

A small electric motor

Think how many machines you have at home that contain an electric motor – vacuum cleaner, washing machine, tape recorder, electric clock, toys. Electric motors also work all underground trains, and many main-line trains as well. They lift us up to the 22nd floor and open automatic doors for us.

Electric motors are quiet, efficient, easy to start or stop and can be very powerful. They all use electricity and magnetism to produce force and movement.

Small electric motors have two main parts – a **magnet** and a revolving **coil** of wire. The wire is usually wound on an iron **core** that can also rotate. When current is fed into the coil it magnetises the core, which is repelled by the magnet and forced to rotate.

Collect

Electric motor
Switch
Power supply
Variable resistor
Construction kit

Build up a motor-driven machine stage by stage.

1. Connect a motor to a switch and a power supply, so that it can be turned on and off.

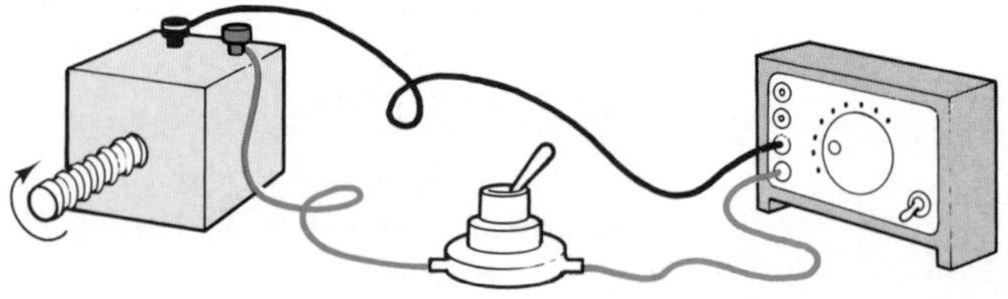

2. Make the motor do a job; for example, pulling up a model lift or driving a fan.
3. Build in a speed control.

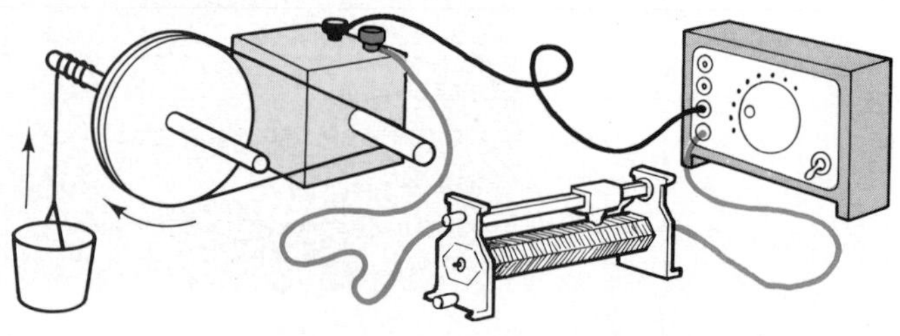

1. Make a drawing of the inside of a small electric motor. Find out the names of the main parts from a reference book and label your picture.
2. Design (on paper) a motor-driven cat flap that only opens for *your* cat. Show how the motor opens the flap and how it is started and stopped by the cat.

CHECKPOINT

B Music from a cone

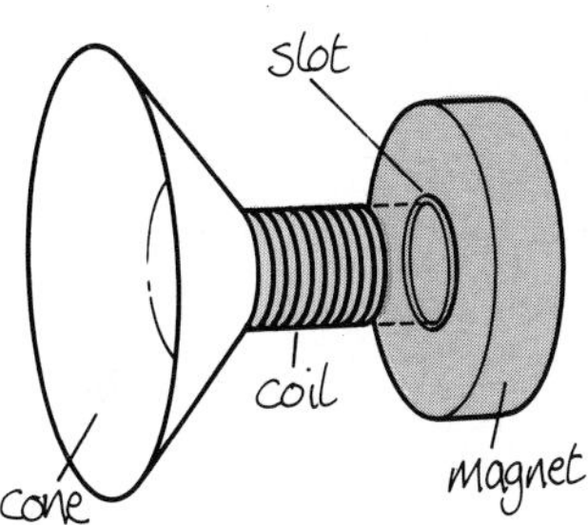

The parts of a loudspeaker

Loudspeakers use the same force as electric motors to make speech and music. They can convert silent electrical signals into loud, realistic sound. Yet they can be made from nothing more than a coil of fine insulated wire, a springy cardboard cone and a circular magnet. The coil is attached to the neck of the cone and fits into a very narrow slot in the magnet. When current is sent through the coil it is forced to move in and out of the slot. This makes the cone, and the air near it, vibrate in and out.

To make sound waves the cone must move in and out rapidly – from about 20 times a second for a low note to 16 000 times a second for a high note. You cannot make the cone jump this quickly by hand, but electrical signals from an amplifier can.

Loudspeakers can be tested with a 'signal generator'. This is an electronic machine that can make a loudspeaker vibrate at particular frequencies.

Collect

Loudspeaker
Signal generator
Battery
Polystyrene beads
Connecting wires

1 Make a loudspeaker jump by connecting wires to it from a battery.
2 Test a loudspeaker.

   a Connect a signal generator to a loudspeaker. Put a handful of polystyrene beads into the cone to show its vibrations.
   b Slowly increase the frequency of the vibrations and watch the beads.
3 Test some other loudspeakers.

1 Write a report on your loudspeaker tests. Describe the movement of the beads at different frequencies.
2 How many loudspeakers have you got at home? (Don't forget there is one in a telephone.)

Gather advertising material, labels from blank cassette-tape boxes, or other material that gives information about different types of audio tapes.

7.3 Sending messages

A Secrets by wire

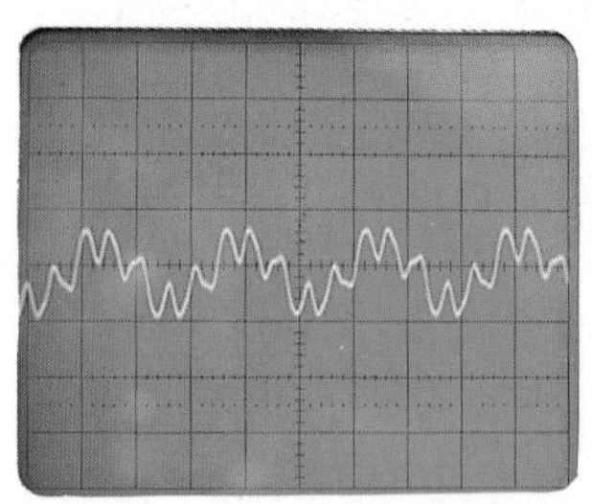

Suppose you want to send a message across the classroom. How could you do it? You could use sound waves and shout. But then everyone else will hear, and if everyone shouts then no one will hear.

Electric waves can carry the message along wires between two loudspeakers. The electric waves can be seen by connecting an oscilloscope to one loudspeaker. They look something like the picture. The waves get larger and smaller and change their shape as the message changes. Signals that carry information by changing continuously like this are called **analogue signals**.

Collect

Drink cans
Thread
Washers
Loudspeakers
Connecting leads

Try these ways of sending secret messages across the room.

1 **Chinese whispers**
Whisper the message to your neighbour and ask him or her to pass it on in a whisper until it reaches your friend.

2 **Tin-can telephone**
Connect two drink cans by strong thread and pass your message by vibrations along the thread.

3 **Electric intercom**
Connect two loudspeakers together with wires. Speak (or sing!) into one and listen at the other.

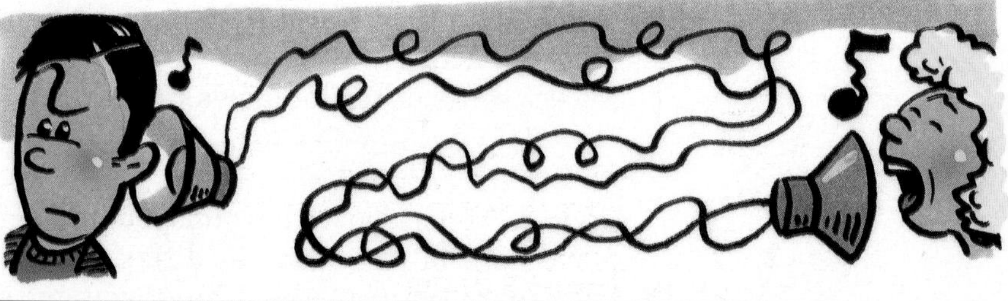

Messages can be sent by code as a series of 'ons' and 'offs'. This is called a **digital signal**. The Morse code is an example of a code you could use to convert the message into digital form. You could use long and short pulses of light to carry the message. The light pulses are either on or off, so this is an example of a digital signal.

Collect

Press-switch
Lamp
Power supply

Send a message by digital code.

1 Make a 'flasher' from a lamp, a press-switch and a voltage supply.
2 Flash a message across the room to a friend. Use the Morse code (see page 145) or invent your own – by giving short and long flashes for the dots and dashes.

1 Make lists of the good points and bad points of each of these ways of sending messages.
2 Think of two things that change continuously with time (like an analogue signal). Write them down.
3 Think of two things in everyday life that come in digital form. Write them down.

B Block talk

Your communication system is made up of different parts with different jobs. These parts can be drawn as blocks joined together to make a block diagram of the whole system.

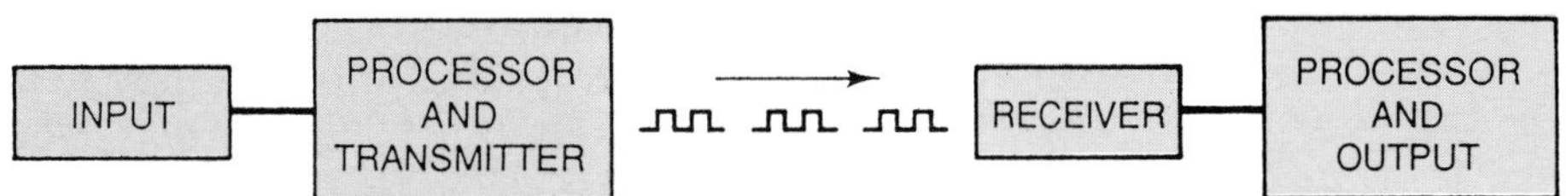

A communication system

Copy the block diagram and use this key to letter the blocks.

a Tariq's brain, arm muscles and pen
b Tariq's eyes
c Nicola's finger
d The switch and lamp

Find out about the binary code for numbers. Make a list of the numbers 0 to 15 in binary code.

A Electronic logic

Electronic circuits are good servants. You switch on the TV and they turn radio signals into pictures. You press the numbers on a telephone and they connect you with a friend. Because they work very quickly, these circuits seem clever, but they wait for you to tell them what to do. Some electronic circuits seem even smarter. They can 'decide' for themselves when to act. Circuits like these need sensors that act as their eyes and ears.

Collect

Electronic kit
Connecting wires
Battery

Use the kit to make some circuits that switch themselves on. Here are three examples (the return parts of the circuits are not shown in the diagrams).

1 It's time to get up

a Connect a light sensor (light-dependent resistor) to a buzzer.

b Reflect some sunshine onto the sensor and the buzzer should tell you its time to get up.

2 Hot breath detector

a Connect a temperature sensor (thermistor) to a buzzer.

b Say 'Haaaa . . .' to the sensor and it will tell you if you have hot breath.

3 Wet nappy detector

a Push two wire probes into a nappy (cloth or tissue) so that they nearly touch. One probe should go to an ON switch and the other to a buzzer.

b Put a drop of water on the nappy near the probes. It should set off the alarm.

AND gates and OR gates are microchips that act as simple brains. They can make simple 'logical' decisions. They both have two inputs and one output, each of which can be either ON or OFF.

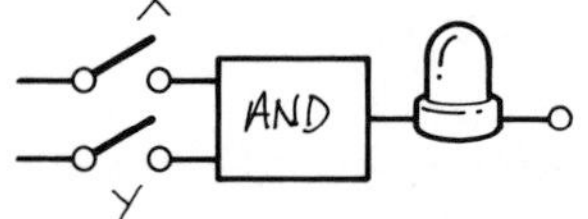

The AND gate works like this
If input X AND input Y are **both** ON, the output goes ON and the lamp lights. No other inputs will light the lamp.

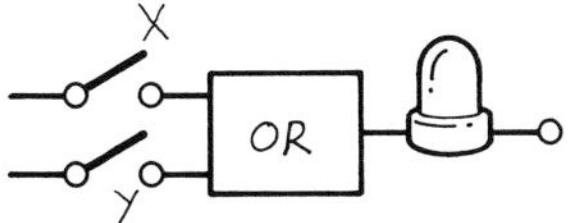

The OR gate works like this
If **either** input X OR input Y is ON, the output goes ON and the lamp lights.

You can use AND and OR gates to invent some very useful electronic gadgets. Here is an example.

A 'latch' or simple memory circuit
An OR gate, with its output connected or 'fed' back to one of its inputs, stays on once it has been triggered. The circuit shown below comes on when the temperature rises and stays on even after the temperature has gone down again. The circuit 'remembers' that it has been hot. Once lit, the lamp 'locks' or 'latches' on.

Collect
Electronics kit
Connecting wires
Battery

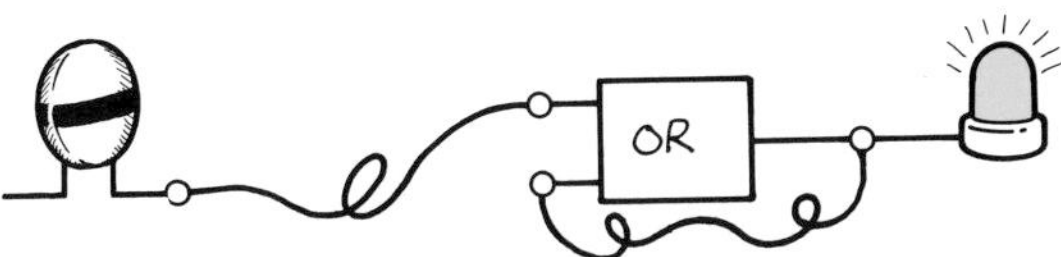

1 Build and test this simple memory circuit.
2 Try it without the feed-back wire.
3 Find out what you must do to 'unlatch' the circuit and turn off the lamp.

1 Explain the difference that the feed-back wire makes to the circuit.
2 Think of a practical use for this circuit.
3 What must you do to turn off the lamp?
4 Design and draw a circuit that will sound a buzzer continuously to give a warning that an increase in temperature has occurred.
5 Make a copy of the 'truth tables' for the logic gates.

CHECKPOINT

B Sensors

A 'NOT gate' is a circuit component (usually an integrated circuit or 'microchip') that reverses things. It would change the wet nappy detector into a dry nappy detector.

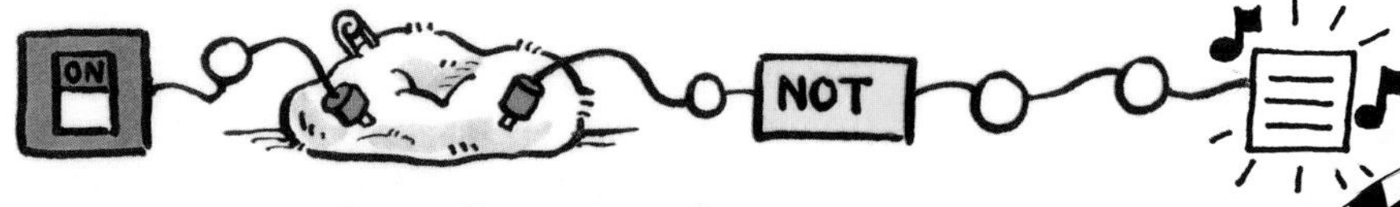

Use this idea to draw diagrams of
a a darkness detector
b a coldness detector.

CHECKPOINT

Make a list of the electronic sensors that you have at home.

7.5 Electrical energy

A Electric charge

If you rub a balloon against your jumper it gets the power to move little objects. It will attract bits of fluff or small pieces of paper and will even stick to you or the ceiling. The balloon picks up an electric charge: it becomes charged with electrical energy.

Collect

Metal tray
Plasticine
Plastic bag

1 Getting a shock from charge

a Press a lump of Plasticine onto a large metal tray.
b Use the Plasticine as a handle and rub the tray over a sheet of plastic.
c Lift the tray and bring it near to your body.

Collect

2 polythene rods
Acetate rod
4 watch glasses
Cloth

2 Forces between charges

a Charge polythene and acetate rods by rubbing with a cloth.
b Balance them on watch glasses so that they can spin freely.
c Bring up a charged polythene rod to each in turn.

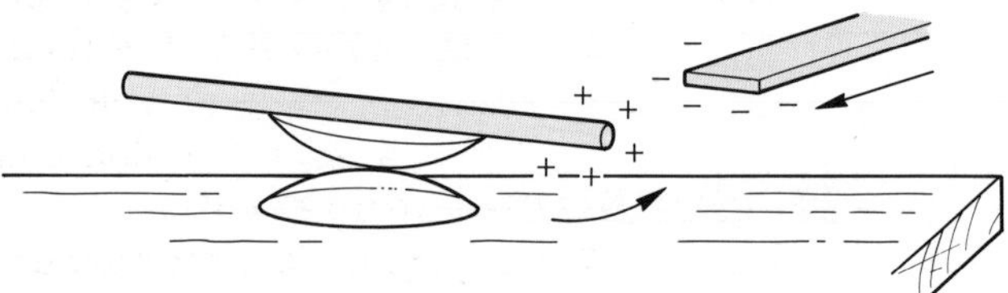

The charge on the polythene is called 'negative' and on the acetate 'positive'.

1 Report on the energy changes that take place in your first investigation.
2 What can you conclude about the forces between electric charges from your second investigation.
3 Copy and complete this table by adding *attract* or *repel.*

	negative charge	positive charge
negative charge		
positive charge		

CHECKPOINT

B Very large charges

A Van de Graaff generator is a machine that can produce large charges at very high voltages. A rubber belt carries negative charge up to a metal dome. The dome is supported on an insulating column so that the charge cannot escape. As the belt runs, more and more charge collects on the dome.

Watch a Van de Graaff machine in action and see what a very large electric charge can do. The charge on the dome can build up a voltage of tens of thousands of volts, so take care not to get too close.

Collect

Van de Graaff machine
Thread
Blu-Tack
Wig
Bunsen burner

Set up the Van de Graaff machine. Your teacher must help you to do the following experiments.

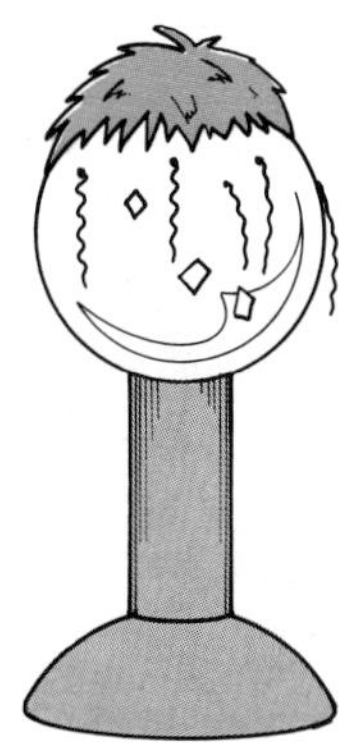

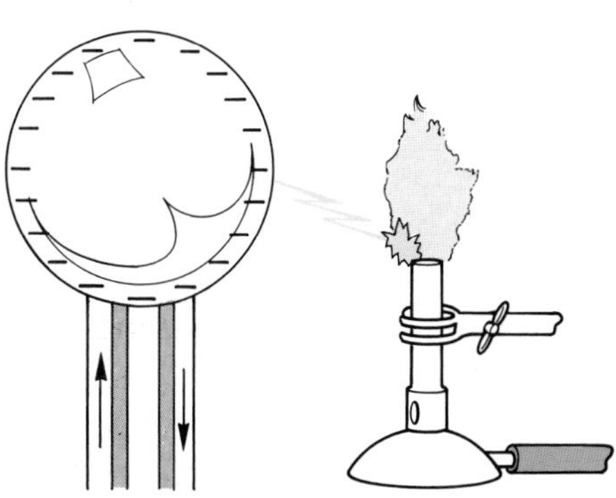

1 Before you charge it up
- put small pieces of paper on the dome
- fix threads on to the dome with Blu-Tack
- put an old wig on the dome (or a volunteer can put their hand on the dome provided they stand on an insulating stool)
- support a Bunsen burner near the dome.

2 Charge up the machine.
a Note what happens to the paper, threads and the hairs of the wig or the volunteer.
b When sparks jump between the dome and the Bunsen burner, turn on the gas supply and see if they are hot enough to light the gas.

Describe each observation you made. Explain each one using what you know about the forces between electric charges.

CHECKPOINT

Obtain pictures and information about lightning and the effects it can have when it strikes aircraft, buildings and people.

7.6 Problem

Mystery tape

Magnetic tape can be used to store information that can then be turned back into its original form whenever we want. Magnetic tape has different names depending on what it is being used for. *Audio tape* stores speech and music, *video tape* stores sound and picture information and *computer tape* stores digital information for the computer memory. Different sizes of tape may be used for these different jobs, but they all work by using magnetic patterns made from electric currents.

Use audio tape to store information in the following ways.

Collect

Tape recorder with microphone
Audio cassette

1 Make an audio-quiz of mysterious sounds.
  - **a** Go around and collect recordings of ten sounds.
  - **b** Follow up the sounds on the tape with the answers to what the sounds were.
  - **c** Try out your quiz on some friends and improve it if necessary.

2 Make a 'mystery person' tape.
  - **a** Choose a friend as the mystery person.
  - **b** Record clues about his or her appearance on the tape: things like height, eye colour, type of hair etc.
  - **c** At the end of the clues give the person's name.
  - **d** Try out the tape on other friends and see how long it takes them to guess the mystery person.

1 How well did the tape store your information?
2 What other equipment would you like so that you could make better-quality mystery tapes?

Quick, easy and clean

Electricity is a very convenient and versatile form of energy. It can give us hot water in minutes, instant light and pop-up toast, or pictures and music at the press of a switch. It does our washing and helps with the housework. Electricity does not cause pollution. However, fuels *are* burnt in far-off power stations. They make our electricity but reduce precious fuel stocks and pollute the air.

Most people in the world have no electricity in their homes. It is either unavailable or too expensive. They must spend a lot more time and effort doing their washing, cooking and cleaning. Other fuels have to be used for heating and they are messy and difficult to use. Without electricity, TVs and stereos cannot be used.

The strip cartoon shows life in the morning in two families; one with electricity and one without.

1 Discuss each frame with your partner. What is happening?
2 Take another part of the day, such as the evening, and discuss the difference electricity makes to the two households then.
3 What should be done to make electricity available to more people? Remember that as fossil fuels run out, electricity made from them will become more expensive. Fewer people will be able to afford electricity.

Geostationary satellites

If you telephone a friend on another continent your message can go either by a cable under the sea or through a communications satellite in space. The journey by satellite is much longer than by cable, and the message has to be coded and sent by radio waves. Even so, it takes less than half a second to travel out to the satellite and back down to your friend on Earth.

The satellites that relay these messages are 35 800 km above the equator and move round in an orbit that takes exactly 1 day. The Earth also rotates once in a day, so the satellites stay above the same place on the equator. This means that from the Earth they seem to be stationary in the sky. Dish antennas can then easily be pointed at the satellites to send and receive messages.

Most communications satellites are in geostationary orbits

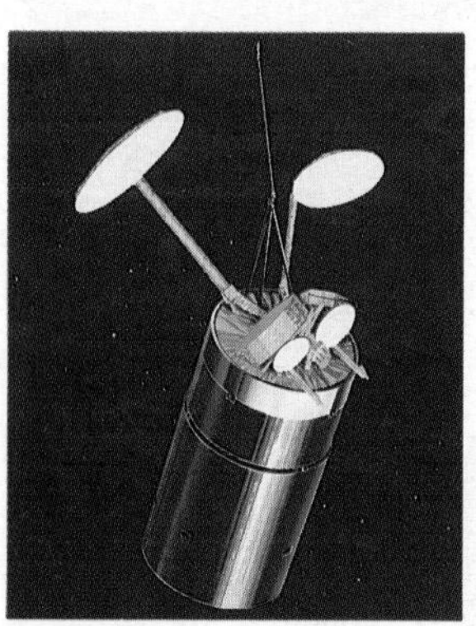

The communications satellite *Intelsat VI F-2*

Intelsat VI F-2 is one such 'geostationary' satellite. It can handle 120 thousand telephone calls and three TV channels at the same time. It is a cylinder about the same size as a railway carriage, with solar panels wrapped around its sides. It weighed about 4.2 tonnes - the weight of a bus - when it was launched from French Guiana in October 1989, and was expected to work for about 13 years. It has fuel on board for thruster rockets to keep it pointing in the right direction. When this fuel runs out, control will be lost and the satellite will be of no further use.

Intelsat VI F-2 has a number of dish and horn antennas that receive signals from Earth, boost them and send them back. Some of them are fixed, and some can be pointed to different spots on the Earth's surface as required. The power to do all this is provided by solar panels and back-up batteries. The total power used by the satellite is 2.2 kW - about the same as a fan heater.

1 Why are dish aerials needed to receive satellite television programmes? In which direction should these dishes be pointed?
2 Geostationary satellites have to be in orbits above the equator. Can you explain why this is so?
3 If a tennis ball represents the Earth, how far away from it would a geostationary satellite have to be on the same scale? (The Earth's radius is about 6400 km.)

8

Make and break

Revision

8.0 The material world

1 Some materials occur **naturally**; some are **synthetic** (made by people).

2 There are different **sources** of raw materials.

Source	Raw material	Examples of use
Air	Gases like oxygen, nitrogen, neon	**1** Breathing apparatus **2** Neon signs
Water	Salt, hydrogen gas, dissolved chemicals	**3** Drinking water **4** Industrial chemicals
Rocks	Metals, metal ores, gemstones	**5** Iron bridges **6** Jewellery
Living things	Enzymes, food chemicals, wood	**7** Food **8** Flavouring
Fossil fuels	Coal, oil, natural gas	**9** Fuel **10** Plastics

3 Raw materials can be **separated** from other substances and **purified** by using techniques like dissolving, filtering, distilling, crystallising or chromatography.

4 Raw materials are changed into synthetic materials by **chemical reactions**.
For example, metal is extracted from rocks by *reduction* processes. Substances like naphtha are separated from crude oil by *fractional distillation* and then *cracked* to make petrol. Some living things *ferment* sugars into alcohol.

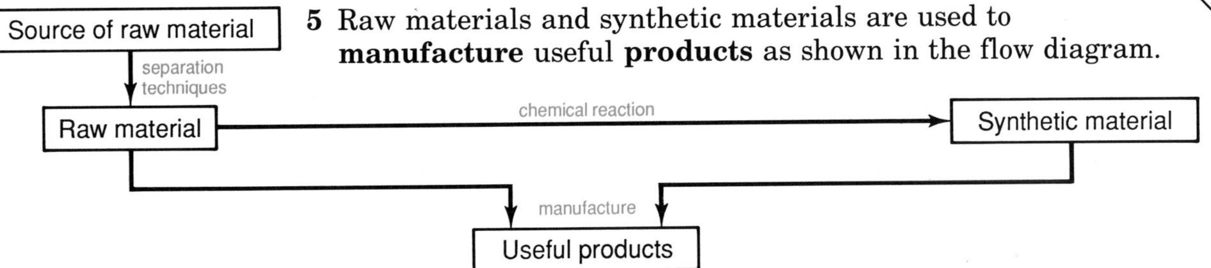

5 Raw materials and synthetic materials are used to **manufacture** useful **products** as shown in the flow diagram.

6 Materials are useful because of their **properties**. For example,

- this material is **strong**

- this material is **hard**

- this material is **flexible**

- this material is **soluble**.

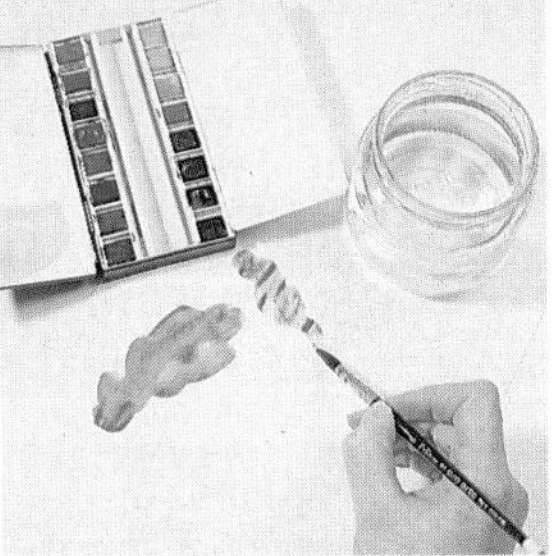

7 Materials can be classified in a number of ways; for example, at room temperature some are **solids**, some **liquids** and some **gases**. Most materials can be changed from one of these states to another by heating or cooling. In each state of matter, the material has a **mass** which can be measured and a **volume** (the space it takes up) which can also be measured.

1 You should know the meaning of the words in **bold**. If you cannot remember what a word means, then look it up in a science book (like *Understanding Science 1* or *2*).

Collect and complete a revision question sheet.

2 Materials are useful. Write a short story that mentions the names and uses of as many materials as you can.

CHECKPOINT

Make a collage of magazine pictures that illustrate useful products manufactured from crude oil.

8.1 Types of materials

A Key materials

Traditional glass

Glass altered by technology

Glass joined in a composite

A **material** is a substance that can be **used**

- to make something
- to do something with.

Materials can be classified in different ways. Different types can look alike and have many similar properties. For example, glass used to be easy to spot; it was see-through and brittle. Now we have optical glass fibres, unbreakable glass, glass wool and so on. We also have plastics that look like glass. In the twentieth century, familiar materials have been altered by technology into new ones. Composite materials, made by joining different types, have been designed to do new jobs. People have even been able to make new types of materials.

This key is a simplified way of classifying materials by using properties that can be observed. It is only a guide and will not be valid for many modern composite materials.

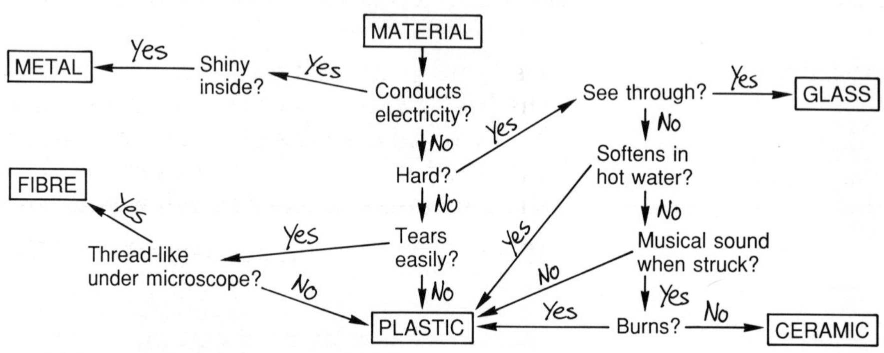

1 **Collect** a set of material samples.
2 Use the key to identify each type of material (you may have to design and do some short practical tests).
3 Record your results in a table with columns for *Sample, Class of material, Common uses.*

1 **a** What is a material? **b** Give names and uses of five materials in the classroom. Write down which class of material each one belongs to.
2 **Collect** and stick a copy of the materials key into your book. Add two examples of each class of material to it.

B Pet insulation

Animals (for example, pet guinea pigs) get heat energy from food. The more heat the animal loses, the more food it has to use up. If the animal loses too much heat then it becomes ill and may die. So heat energy is valuable and it should not be wasted. Many animals are well insulated to keep the heat energy inside their bodies. People also have some insulation but it is not very efficient. We have therefore designed and used materials to help keep heat inside our bodies and also inside our houses and other objects. We can use this technology to help our pets keep warm too.

Some examples of animals with good heat insulation

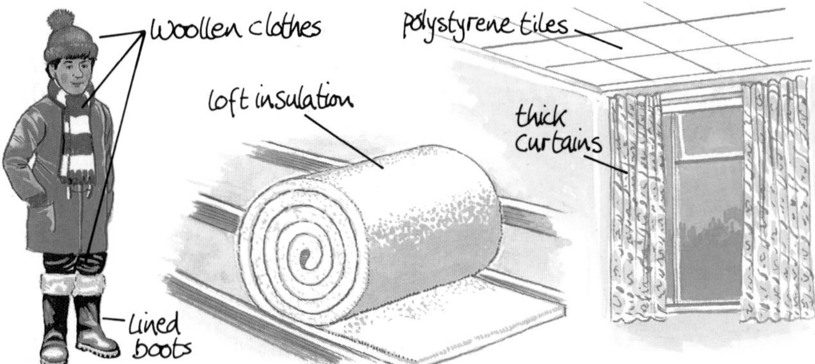

Some examples of objects with good heat insulation

Collect

Samples of materials
Thermometer
Anything else you need

Use your general knowledge and the pictures above to find the best material for insulating a guinea pig's hutch. You will have to design, plan and carry out an *investigation* into the insulating properties of suitable materials. Discuss the four areas illustrated below with your group.

If you are totally stuck then ask for help from your teacher.

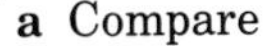

a Compare **b** Control the variables **c** Measure **d** Record

Describe your investigation on a poster which covers the four areas given above. Each member of the group should produce a different section of the poster.

CHECKPOINT

Visit a DIY shop to collect a leaflet (or consult magazines for information) about the materials used to insulate people's homes.

8.2 The property pages

A Baby wear

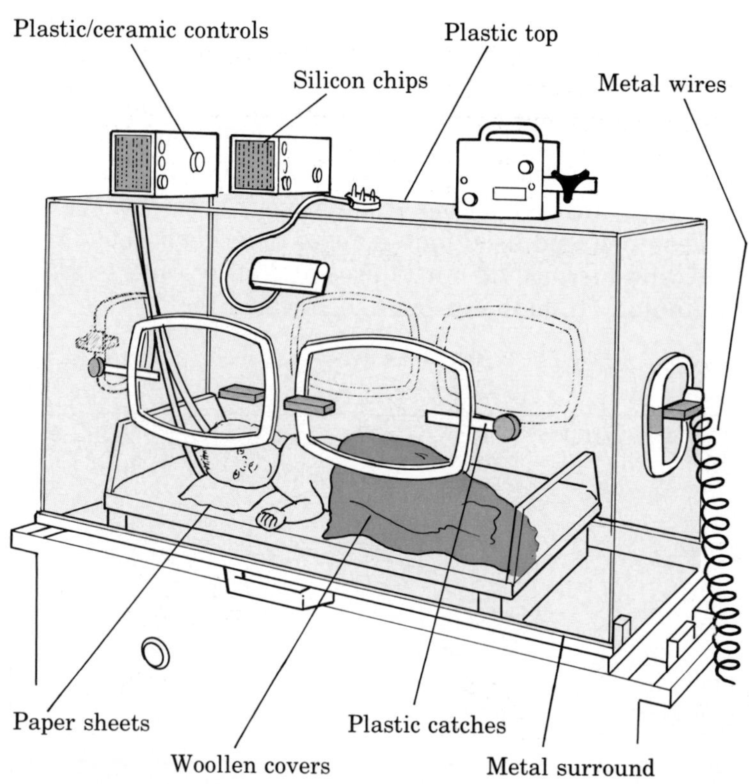

The use that is made of a material depends on its properties. This incubator is made of many different materials, each one chosen to do a particular job.

Each material has been tested to make sure that it is suitable for the job it has to do. For example, the plastic top will have been tested for strength to make sure it protects the baby underneath. The fuse wire in the electrical circuits will have been tested to check that it melts if too much current goes through the circuits.

Collect

Either 3 types of wool
or 3 types of filling
Anything else you need

You have to design and carry out tests to find the best material to use in **one** of the following:

a a pair of baby mittens
b the filling in a disposable nappy.

Your group will have to discuss and decide

1. which properties are most important
2. how these properties can be tested
3. how any comparison can be made fair.

1. Why are the properties of a material important?
2. Describe how you investigated the baby-wear material. Make clear which properties you were testing and what the results of your investigation were.
3. Use a dictionary (or your own knowledge) to write a definition of each of the properties: *strength, hardness, elasticity, flammability.*
4. What property must each of the materials used by the climber have?

B Desirable property for sale

Collect

Set of advert cards
Poster paper
Glue

Do not cut this book!

The object on each advert card is for sale because it contains a material with the property named.

1 Collect a set of cards, cut them out, shuffle them and deal them out between everyone in the group.
2 To each of your cards add a short slogan or sentence to explain why the named property is desirable.
3 Stick the cards onto poster paper for display.

a Strong	**b** Soluble	**c** Hard	**d** Soft
e Flexible	**f** Low density	**g** High density	**h** Waterproof
i Heat insulator	**j** Electrical insulator	**k** Heat conductor	**l** Non-flammable
m Elastic	**n** High melting point	**o** Electrical conductor	**p** Rigid

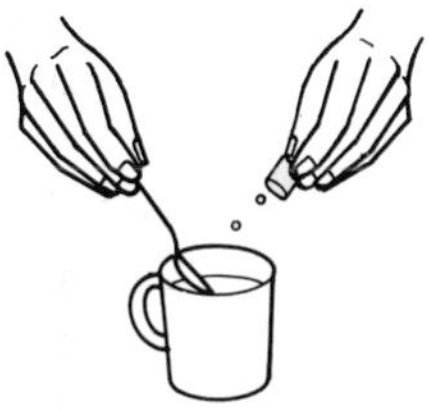

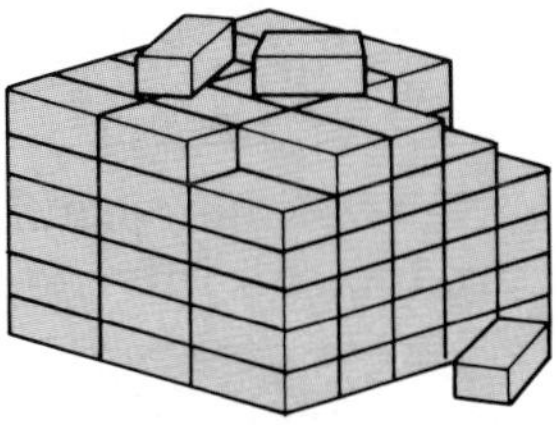

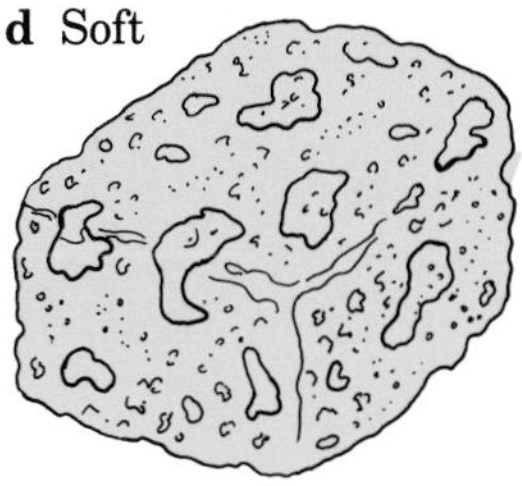

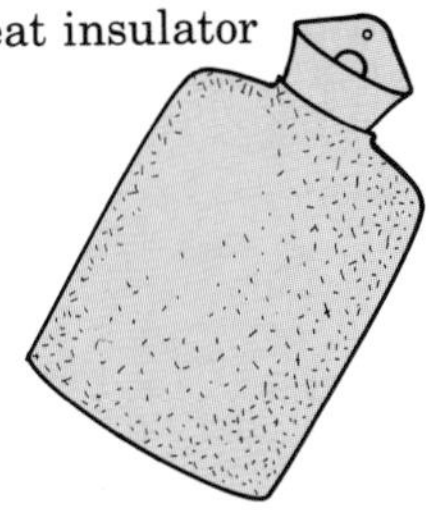

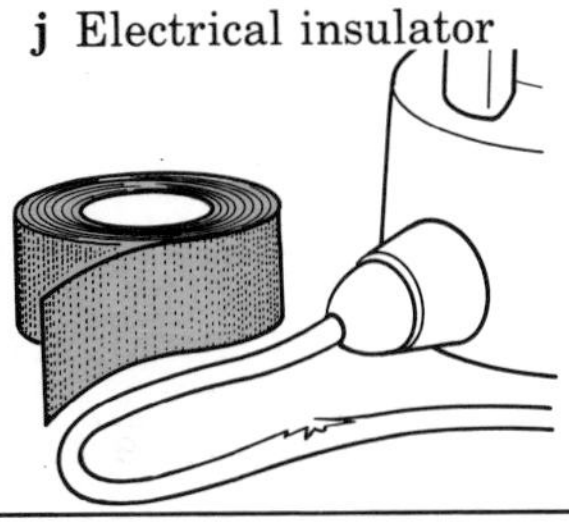

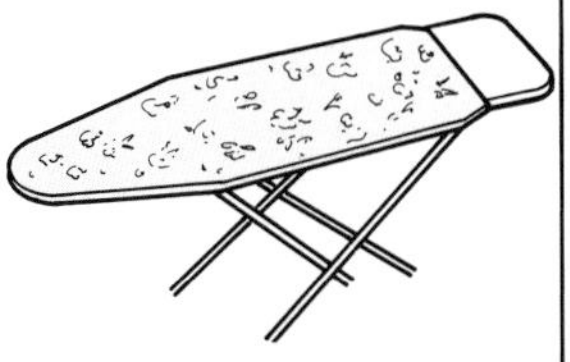

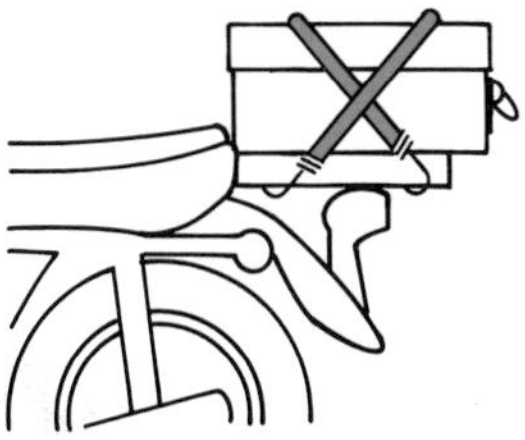

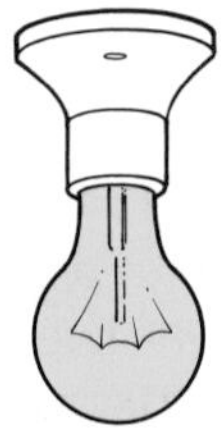

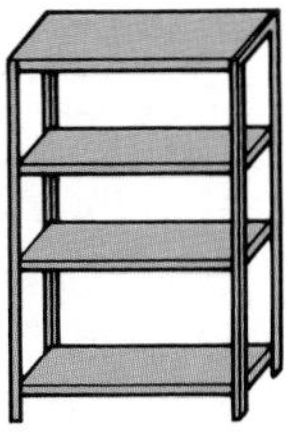

CHECKPOINT

Obtain three labels or packets that describe the properties of the product that is being sold.

8.3 Destroyed by fire

A Flammable

Many materials are **flammable**; they can be set on fire. Once on fire, a material will produce a lot of heat energy. It will also react and **decompose**, which means that the molecules of the material will break up into smaller molecules. For example, some materials burn to produce a lot of smoke which can suffocate a person. Many synthetic materials decompose in a fire to make poisonous gases which can kill in minutes.

Synthetic material	Used in	Produces poisonous
Polyurethane foam	Some furniture	Hydrogen cyanide
Polystyrene	Ceiling tiles/insulation	Carbon monoxide
Rubber	Carpet lining	Sulphur dioxide
PVC	Chair coverings/tiles	Hydrogen chloride

The two photographs show how quickly a smouldering object can produce an inferno of heat, thick smoke and poisonous fumes.

After 30 seconds

After 3 minutes

In house fires it is much more likely that a person will be overcome by smoke and gas than by flames. This is why all firefighters say that you should have a smoke alarm in the house.

1 **Collect** and examine the smoke alarm. Read the instruction booklet and find out how this sensor works.
2 Design a **safe** experiment to test the alarm.
Show your design to your teacher.
Test your design, using a fume cupboard if necessary.

1 Describe the effects of the fire
a in the first photograph **b** in the second photograph above.
2 What are the major dangers to a person in a house fire?
3 Describe your investigation of the smoke alarm.
What is your opinion of the alarm?
4 Apart from an alarm, what other precautions should people take to protect themselves against fire in their homes? (You will find some ideas and information in the leaflets/books in class.)

CHECKPOINT

B Non flammable

- Some materials are flammable

- Some are non flammable

Sometimes the property of a material can be changed by treatment. For example, flammable materials like cotton can be chemically treated to make them less likely to catch fire. The material is then said to be flameproof.

Collect

Stand
Wire
Stapler
Bunsen burner and heatproof mat
Timer
Paper strip
Safety glasses

Your teacher has divided a piece of fabric into two equal parts and flameproofed **one** of the pieces. The other piece can be used as a control.

1 **Collect** a small piece of flameproofed and of control fabric.
2 Test each piece as follows.

1 Staple a paper strip to the piece of fabric

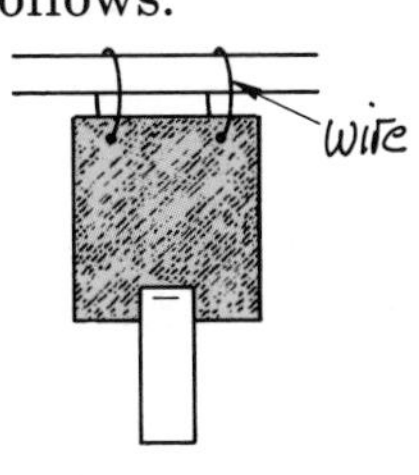

2 Attach the other end to the stand

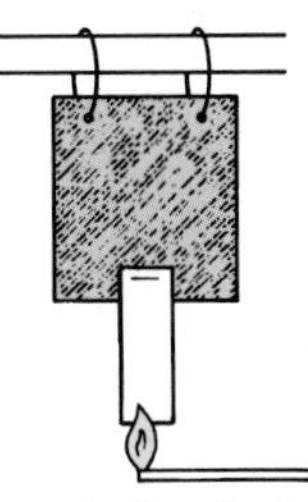

3 Light the bottom of the paper strip

4 Time how long the fabric burns (or smoulders)

3 Test any other fabrics available in the same way, and record the results in a table.

1 What does *flammable* and *flameproofed* mean?
2 Write a report about your investigation (using a word processor if possible).
3 How did flameproofing affect the flammability of the other fabrics?

Visit a furniture store or a clothes shop and find out if any merchandise contains flameproofed fabrics.

CHECKPOINT

8.4 Damaged by the weather

A Rot and crumble

Fire causes materials to burn (combust) and decompose very quickly.

However materials can also change quite slowly, rotting and losing properties like great strength, waterproofing, flexibility and so on. Temperature changes, rain water and wind can help

- metal to corrode
- wood to rot
- stone to crumble

The effects of weather on a material can be investigated in the laboratory. This experiment **simulates** (imitates) the effects of rain and air on various metals

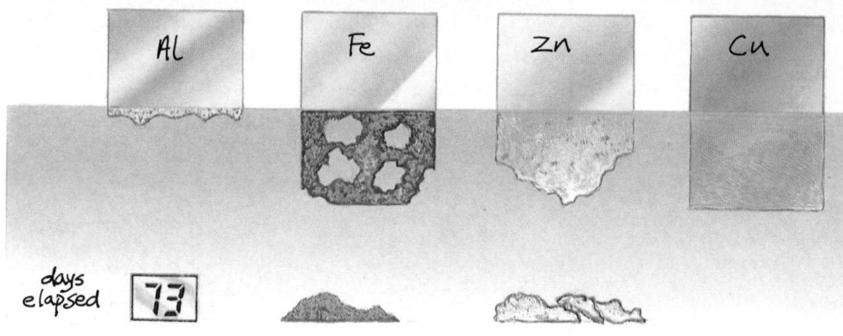

Look at the samples of weathered materials which have been left outside for several months.
Compare the weathered samples with fresh samples using
a your unaided eyes **b** a microscope or a hand lens
c simple tests of flexibility, hardness and strength.

1. From the evidence in the picture above, what do air and water do to metals like iron.
2. Describe the effects of the weather on the appearance and properties of the samples of materials.
3. Natural materials like wood are often decomposed by living things which feed on them. If you have time, use the books in the classroom to find out about the living things that cause wood to rot. Key words to look up are *dry rot, wet rot, woodworm, fungus.* Write a few sentences about your findings.

CHECKPOINT

B Rust protection

paint

chrome electroplating

grease

Iron is a very useful material. Unfortunately it corrodes easily in air and water. Corrosion of iron is called rusting. It costs lots of money because the iron loses its strength as it turns into new compounds, mainly iron oxide.

There are different ways of protecting a metal from corrosion.

Keep water and air away

Cover with a thin layer of another metal

Mix metals to form an alloy

Use electricity

Investigate one (or more) of the questions on the cards below. For each investigation, **collect** and follow the investigation card. The card lists the equipment that you need and gives some hints about which methods to try out.
In all the investigations use rust indicator to show up the corrosion of iron. Use salt water to make the rusting faster than it would otherwise be.
Record your results by

a copying the diagram on the investigation card

b answering the investigation question.

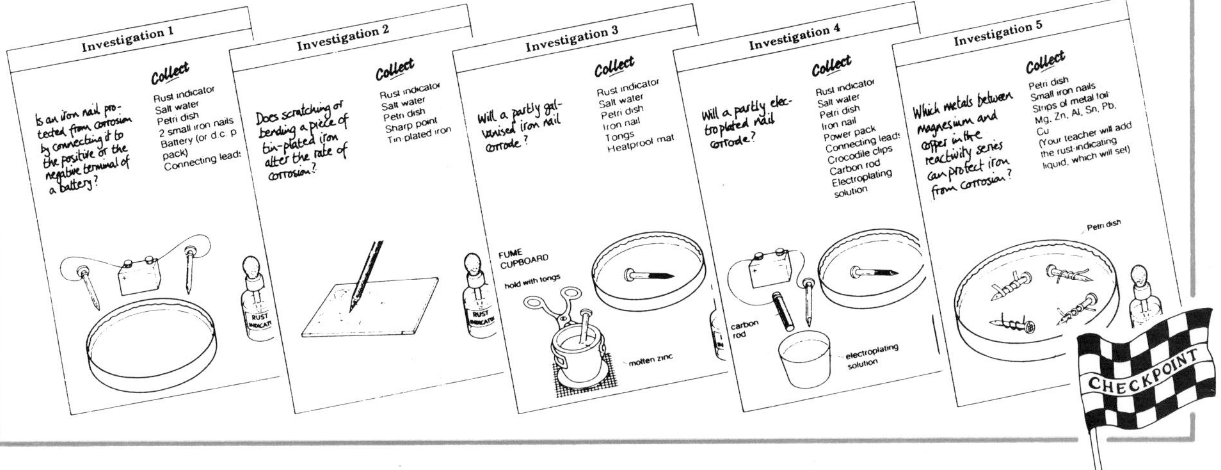

Inspect your own home and school. Make a note of the materials that have been damaged by the weather. Take a few photographs if you can.

Changeable materials

A Altering the property

The properties of a material can be altered.

- A material can be treated to change its properties.
- A material can undergo a chemical reaction which changes its properties.

Clothing for fire fighters is made from fabric specially treated to give maximum protection against heat

Synthetic materials can be altered to give different properties – expanded polystyrene has ideal properties for packaging

Heat changes the properties of dough

Filler reacts with the air and hardens

Exposure to heat and water causes paint to blister and peel

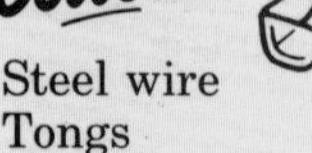

Collect

Steel wire
Tongs
Beaker
Bunsen burner and heatproof mat
Safety glasses

Collect

20 cm^3 acidified water
Universal indicator
Burette
Alkali
Conical flask
White tile

1 a Hold the wire with tongs and bend it to test its flexibility.
  b Heat the wire until it is red hot.
  c Drop it into a beaker of cold water. The steel is now said to be *tempered.*
  d Test the tempered steel for flexibility.

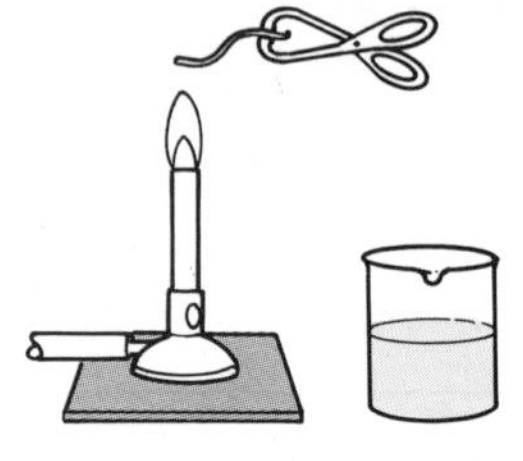

2 a Fill the burette with alkali.
  b Put exactly 20 cm^3 of acidified water into the conical flask. Add a few drops of universal indicator. It will show the pH of the water.
  c Add the alkali to the acidified water a little at a time. When the indicator changes to green, the solution has become *neutral.*

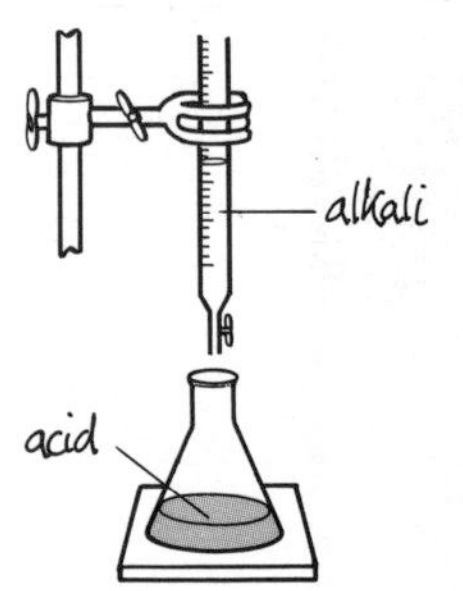

1 Why should people want to change the properties of materials?
2 a Describe how you changed one property of steel.
  b What could tempered steel be used for?
3 a Describe how you changed one property of acid water.
  b When could neutralisation of acidified water be useful?

CHECKPOINT

B Neutralisation

An acid can be changed by the chemical reaction of **neutralisation**.

In a neutralisation reaction, the **acid** reacts with a **neutraliser** (for example, a **base**).

When an acid is neutralised, a compound called a **salt** is formed.

acid + neutraliser → salt + water (or hydrogen)

Salts are very useful substances. The following are all salts.

- *sodium chloride* – used as flavouring and preservative
- *ammonium phosphate* – used as fertiliser
- *silver bromide* – used in photographic film
- *potassium nitrate* – used as a preservative in some meats

Collect

$20\ cm^3$ sulphuric acid
Copper carbonate
Beaker
Filter funnel
Filter paper
Crystallising dish
Heatproof mat

Use the following procedure to make copper sulphate.

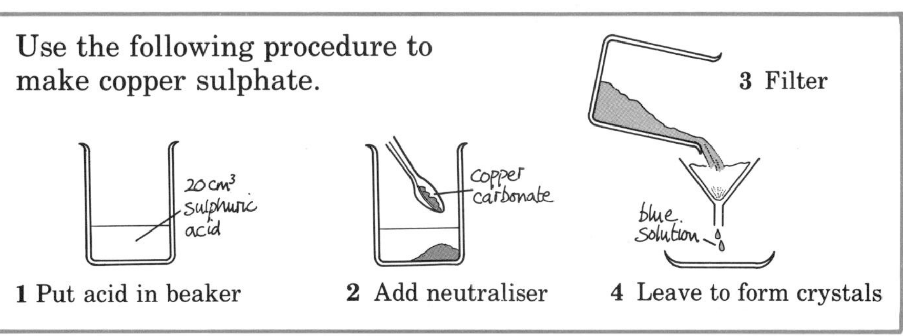

1 Describe your experiment using the words *acid, neutraliser* and *neutralisation* in your description.

2 Explain what is happening in each of the cartoons. Give the name of the *acid* and the *neutraliser* in each case.

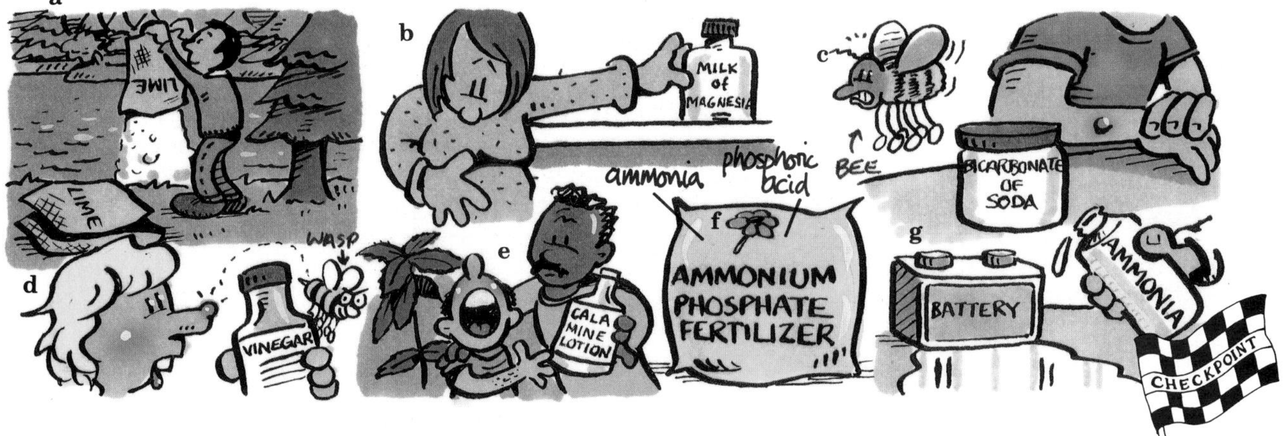

During the next few days, as you watch TV or read magazines, look out for examples of chemical reactions which change the properties of a material. Note the details of the programmes or articles.

8.6 Problem

Piles of tiles

Your problem is to find out which floor tile would be best in a kitchen. Some likely difficulties with tiles are highlighted in the picture below.

1 Hot food splashes from the cooker and causes damage
2 Fridge and cooker leave dents
3 Water is splashed and makes the floor slippery
4 The surface is scuffed
5 Blackcurrant juice is spilt and stains the tiles
6 Dirt from the garden sticks to the tiles

Collect

Tiles
Any equipment you need

1 Discuss the properties that a good kitchen tile must have. Make a list of at least four important properties.
2 You have to find out which of the tiles is best for a kitchen floor.
Design and carry out **fair** experiments to **compare** the properties of the tiles. If you are not sure of what to do then ask for the *Hints sheet.*
This will give you a picture hint for several possible property tests.
3 Record your results in a table like the one below (✓✓✓ means excellent, ✓✓ means good, ✓ means adequate).

Property	Tile A	Tile B	Tile C
Flexibility	✓✓✓	✓	✓✓
and so on...			

Write a full report about your investigation which
- describes each test (including a diagram)
- mentions how you controlled the variables
- includes a table of results
- gives your conclusion.

8.7 Talkabout

Every picture tells a story

The following charts, diagram and table tell a modern story in four parts about fossil fuels. Discuss each part in your group. Decide the answer(s) to each question. One person from the group should write down your group's answer to part 1, a different person write the answer to part 2 and so on.

Part 1 is about the **raw materials**.
The bars on the graph are in blocks of three. Compare the bars within each block and between each block. What does this bar graph tell you?

Part 2 is about the **immediate use** of these raw materials. Compare the size of the two pie charts and the size of the slices within each one. What do these pie charts tell you?

Part 3 is about **making new materials** from the raw materials. The diagram is about crude oil. What does the diagram tell you?

Part 4 is about **using up** the new materials.
Compare the figures for 1983 and 1988 and also the change column which compares 1988 with 1987. What do these figures mean?

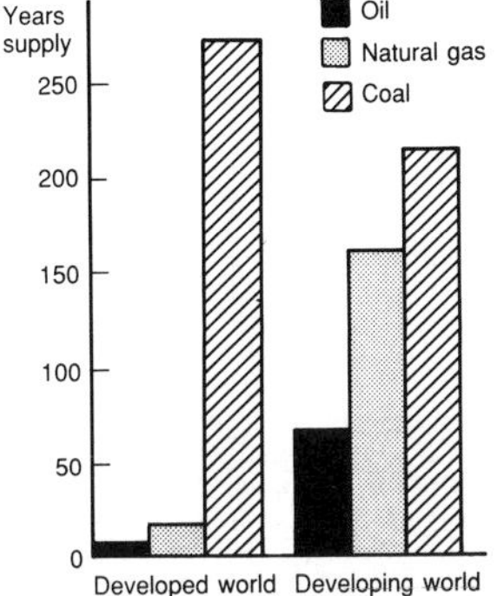

Part 1 Number of years' supply of fossil fuels remaining

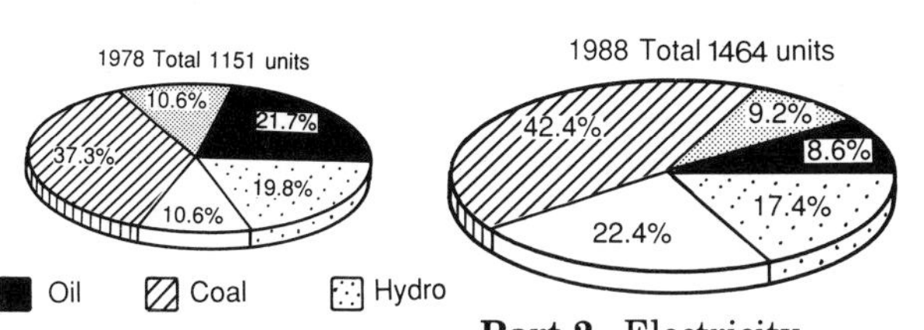

Part 2 Electricity generated by different fuel types

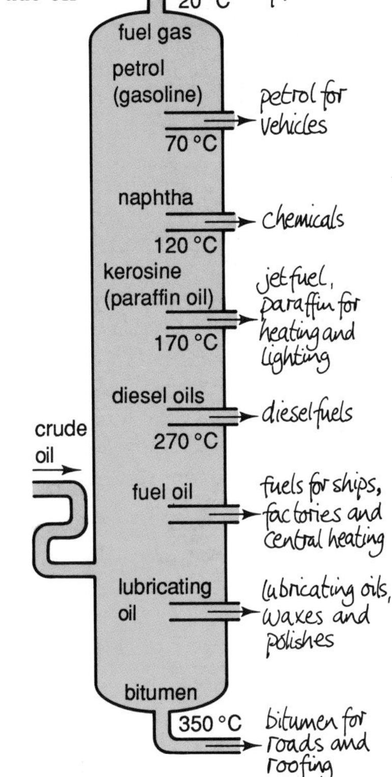

Part 3 Fractional distillation of crude oil

Part 4 Use of main oil products (millions of tonnes)

	1983	1984	1985	1986	1987	1988	Change 1988 over 1987	1988 share of total
Western Europe								
Gasoline	135.2	135.5	135.6	142.0	144.7	147.5	+1.9%	24.8%
Middle distillates	213.1	221.3	223.9	234.8	236.7	240.3	+1.5%	40.4%
Fuel oil	135.2	128.5	117.9	118.5	113.5	121.3	+6.9%	20.4%
Others	88.2	91.1	87.2	91.8	90.6	85.0	−6.2%	14.4%
Total Western Europe	571.7	576.4	564.6	587.1	585.5	594.1	+1.5%	100.0%
Developing World								
Gasoline	104.6	105.2	112.2	112.9	115.2	120.4	+4.5%	18.3%
Middle distillates	214.5	218.4	223.9	227.1	240.4	253.9	+5.6%	38.5%
Fuel oil	167.5	168.4	165.5	169.4	170.4	180.0	+5.6%	27.3%
Others	81.3	85.0	85.8	92.2	100.1	104.8	+4.8%	15.9%
Total Developing World	568.0	577.0	587.4	601.6	626.1	659.1	+5.3%	100.0%

Note: 'Gasoline' consists of aviation and motor fuels. 'Middle distillates' consist of jet and burning kerosines, and gas and diesel oils. 'Fuel oil' includes ship fuel. 'Others' consist of gases, solvents, lubricants, bitumen, wax, etc.

Breaking up substances with electricity

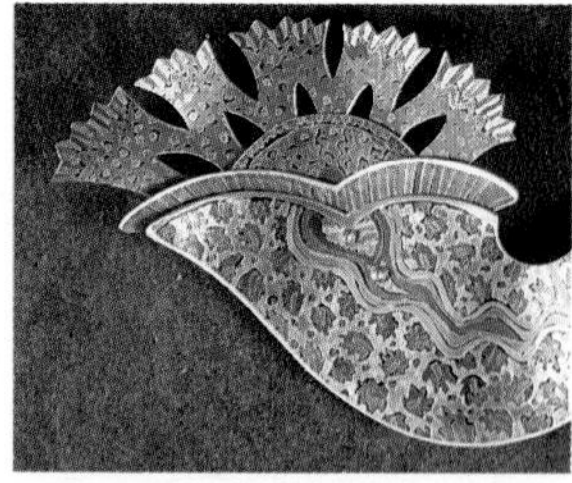

Electricity is a versatile form of energy. It is used in some industries to split compounds up to form useful materials.

Electricity is used to cause the changes printed in blue.

Piece of bauxite → aluminium foil → dyed anodised aluminium

Salt → chlorine → plastics, solvents, disinfectants, insecticides

Salt → sodium → separating titanium, indigo dye

Salt → sodium hydroxide → soaps, detergents, paper, fibres

Salt → hydrogen → fuel, margarine

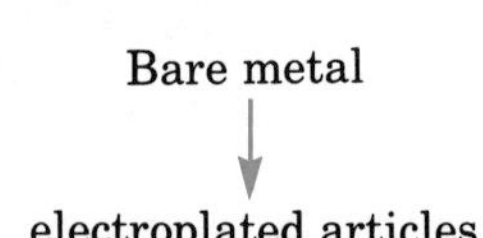

Electricity is so useful because it can separate elements from **ionic** compounds. As you saw in topic 6.5, the ions become free to move when the substance is dissolved or molten. Electricity then makes the ions move and the compound splits up. We say that **electrolysis** has occurred. Any compound which will conduct electricity when molten or dissolved is known as an **electrolyte**.

In a molten substance the metal ion is positively charged and so is attracted to the negative electrode. The non-metal ion is negatively charged and so is attracted to the positive electrode

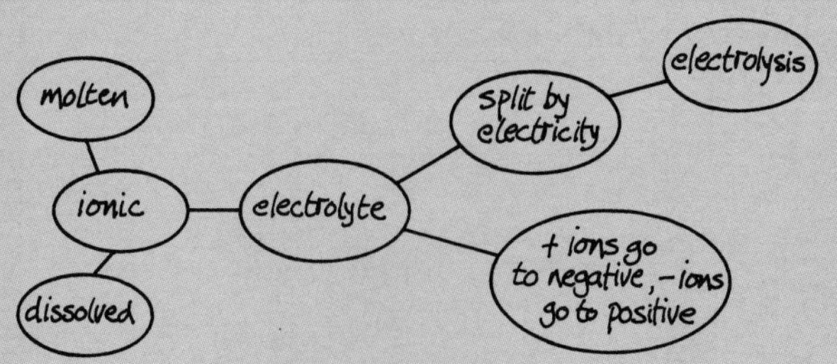

In a solution of the substance in water, the ions move in the same way. However, the water is also separated by the electricity. Hydrogen gas may be produced at the negative electrode. Oxygen gas may bubble off the positive electrode

Your teacher will provide some resources which contain information about the uses of electricity in industry.

1 Find the information and read it.
2 Summarise the important information in a spider diagram like the one above.

The key words below will help you to search the booklets, videos or perhaps even a computer data base like *Campus 2000*.

Electrolysis, industry, chlorine, aluminium, electrowinning, sodium chloride, brine, anodising, copper, zinc, sodium, electrolytic decomposition

Extensions

Mineral requirements for plants

Plants make food molecules by the process of photosynthesis, but they also get important compounds from the soil. These contain essential minerals and if they are missing then the plant will become unhealthy. A plant's appearance often gives clues about which essential minerals are missing.

Four of these plants are unhealthy. Discuss the evidence of this in each case.

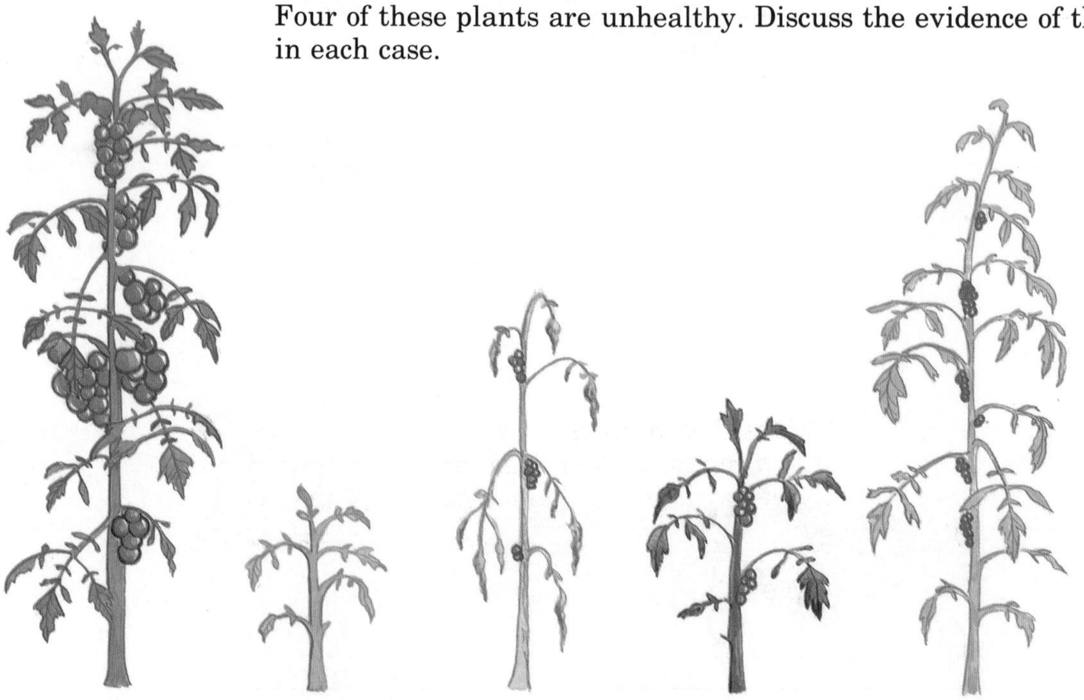

a Full diet **b** Diet lacking nitrogen **c** Diet lacking potassium **d** Diet lacking phosphorous **e** Diet lacking magnesium

1 All these plants were grown in the same controlled environment. For example, the amount of light was kept constant. What other variables would be kept constant?
2 Plant **a** has been given all the essential minerals that it needs. It is called a '**control**' in this experiment. Explain why a control is necessary.
3 Compared to the control, what variable has been changed in experiment **b**? What are the differences between the appearance of this plant and the control?
4 Repeat question 3 for plants **c, d** and **e**.
5 Why do fertilisers contain the elements nitrogen, potassium and phosphorus?

A good suit, a good fit

Living things, or **organisms**, are adapted to their environment. An organism survives best in a particular kind of habitat. On the other hand it may not be able to survive at all in other kinds of habitat.

Lichens are a good example. The type of lichen that grows in a habitat depends on how clean the air is. They are therefore good indicators of air pollution, as shown in the table.

Type of lichen	Level of pollution by sulphur dioxide (SO_2)	
crusty blue-green	125 micro grams/m^3 of air	high pollution
crusty yellow	70 $\mu g/m^3$	↕
leafy blue-green	60 $\mu g/m^3$	
shrubby blue-green	40 $\mu g/m^3$	
mossy blue-green	30 $\mu g/m^3$	low pollution

This is *Pleurococcus*.
It is a common green alga, and can grow in polluted and clean air.
You can find it growing on trees and walls and large rocks.

Investigate the distribution of *Pleurococcus* in the school grounds. Look for a pattern. Think about moisture, the direction that it faces, type of surface, height, and other variables.
Make any measurements that you can.
Suggest a hypothesis to explain the distribution you observe.
Test your hypothesis by looking for *Pleurococcus* in
- places you expect to find it
- places you do not expect to find it.

Think about any necessary changes to your hypothesis.

1 Describe the results of your survey. Include a hypothesis to explain the distribution.
2 Why are lichens good pollution indicators? Draw a bar chart showing type of lichen against level of pollution.

Plant factories

Green plants make their own food. They use light from the Sun to power the process called photosynthesis. A substance called **chlorophyll** changes light energy into a form of energy that can be used in the chemical reactions of photosynthesis. The small molecule produced is glucose – a sugar. This can be used to make a range of polymers essential to the plant.

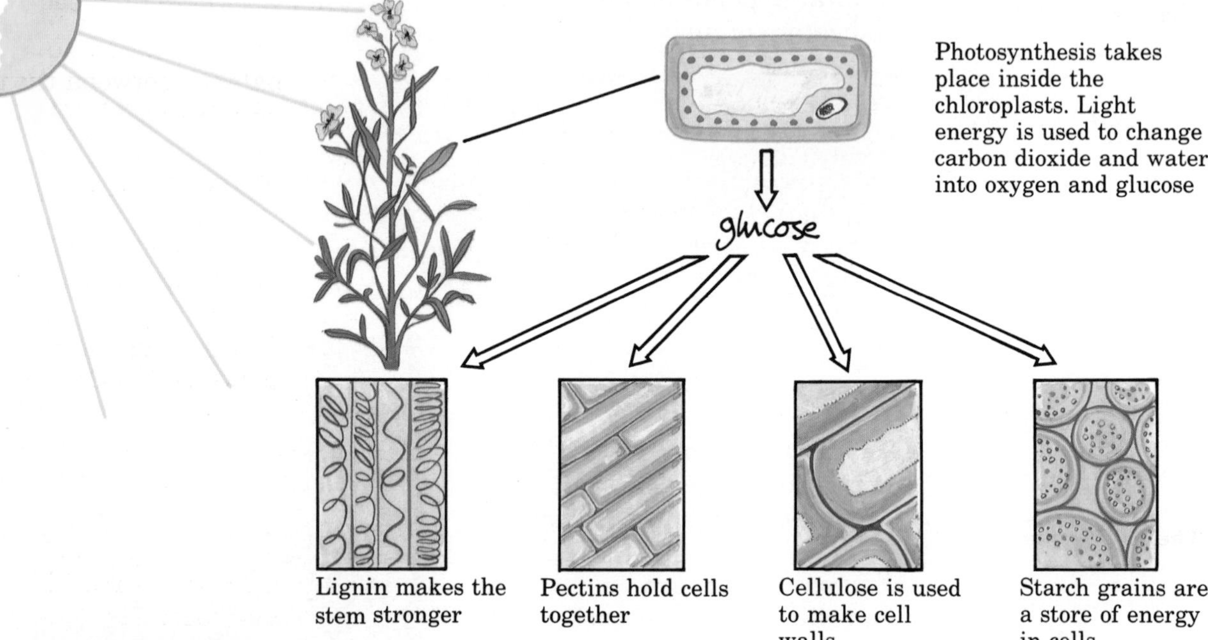

Collect

Seeds
Iodine solution
Plant stem material
Potato
Scalpel
Microscope
Microscope slides

1 Test the seeds for the presence of starch (look for a blue/black colour with iodine).
2 Prepare a microscope slide of a thin slice of potato tissue. Stain this with iodine.
3 Prepare a microscope slide of the stem material.

1 Write down a word equation for photosynthesis.
2 Why is chlorophyll essential for photosynthesis?
3 Name four plant materials made from glucose. Explain why they are essential to the plant.
4 Make a table with suitable headings and title to show the results of your starch test on seeds.
5 Make a drawing of what you saw on each of your microscope slides.
Label starch grains on the potato drawing.
Label cellulose cell walls and lignin on the stem drawing.

The cycle of elements

There are 92 naturally occurring elements. Many are required by living things in tiny amounts. However, four major elements are required to form the tissues of all living things. These are hydrogen, oxygen, carbon and nitrogen. For life on Earth to continue the available amounts of these essential elements must remain steady. They are recycled through the ecosystem.

The carbon cycle

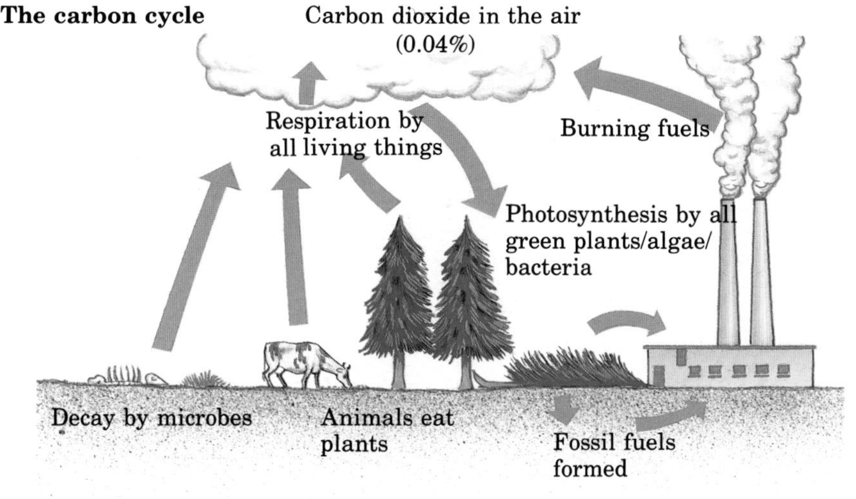

Carbon and oxygen are recycled by the balance between the processes of respiration and photosynthesis. The activities of humans seem to be upsetting the balance of this cycle. The consequences could be drastic.

The nitrogen cycle

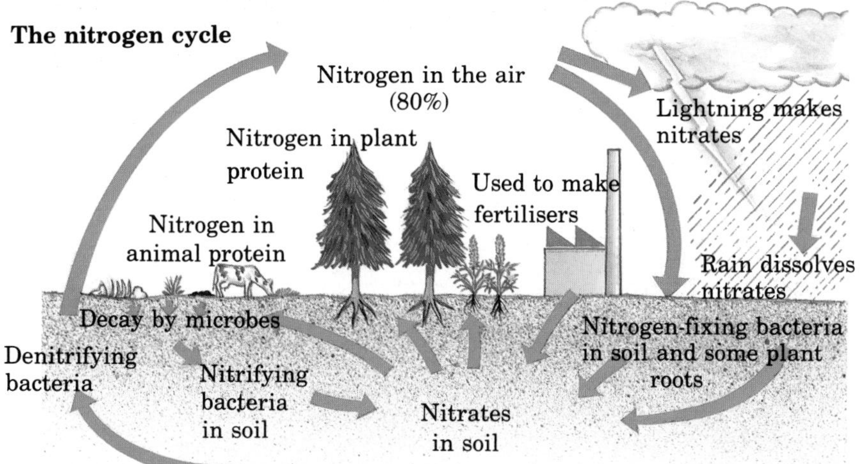

Nitrogen is recycled in a more complicated way, involving several different processes. The activities of humans may be upsetting this cycle too.

1 **Collect** and complete copies of the carbon and nitrogen cycles, and stick them into your book.
2 Describe how the activities of people are causing problems in
  - the carbon cycle
  - the nitrogen cycle.
3 What do you think could be done to
  a keep the amount of carbon dioxide in the air at a low level?
  b keep enough nitrogen compounds in garden soil?

Water pollution

You need water. You drink it. You wash in it, and you use it to clean other objects. Huge amounts of water are also used in industry for cooling and for cleaning. Water dissolves many substances and so it can easily become polluted. The diagram shows several common sources of water pollution in the UK.

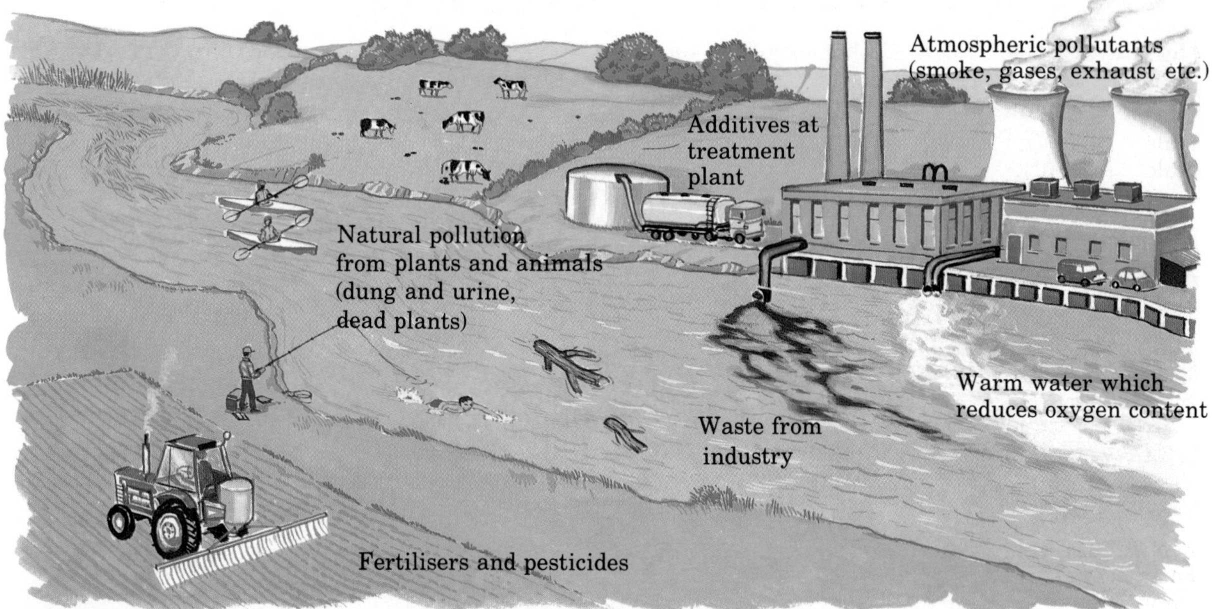

Collect

Sample of stream water
Sample of rain water
Water pollution kit

1. Look for obvious pollution in the two water samples; for example, plant and animal material, mud, soot and so on. Use a microscope if one is available.
2. Ask your teacher to show you how the oxygen meter operates. Use the meter to measure the oxygen content of the two water samples.
3. Measure the pH of the water samples. Use either a pH meter or a piece of universal indicator paper.
4. Test the water samples for chloride and for sulphate/sulphite contamination.
5. You may be able to find other tests to try out. Look for these in chemistry books. Key words to look up in the index are *water pollution, testing for.*

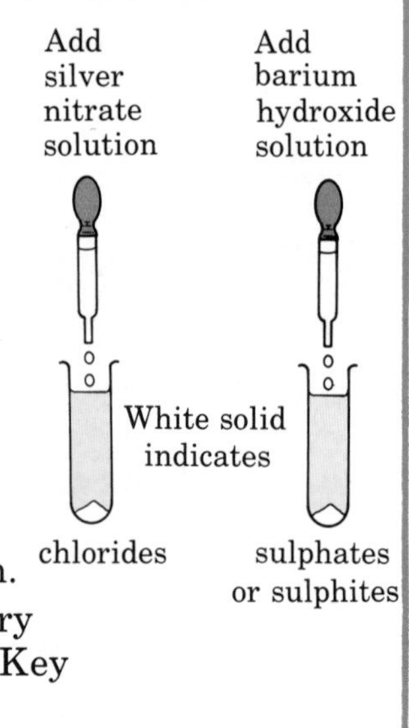

Write a report comparing the pollution (if any) of the two samples.

Girl or boy?

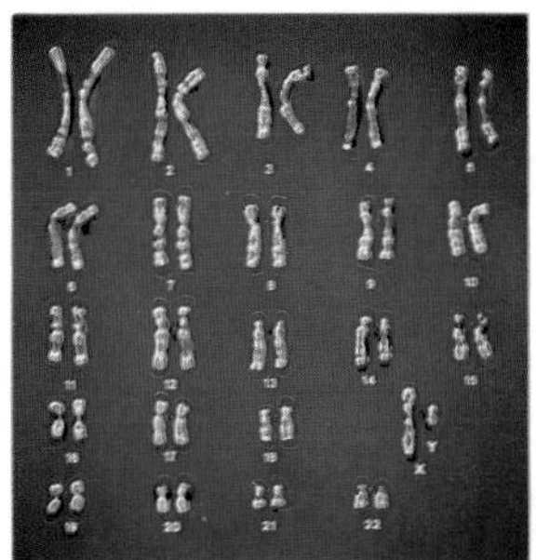
Male chromosome set. Males have one X and one Y sex chromosome

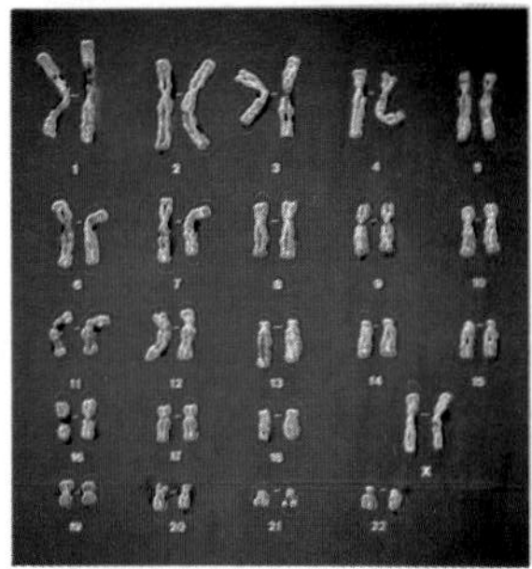
Female chromosome set. Females have two X sex chromosomes

It is possible to discover the sex of an unborn baby. The doctor removes a little of the liquid that surrounds the baby in the womb. Cells in this liquid are examined with a microscope. Thread-like structures can be seen in the nucleus. These are chromosomes. A single chromosome is made up of thousands of genes.

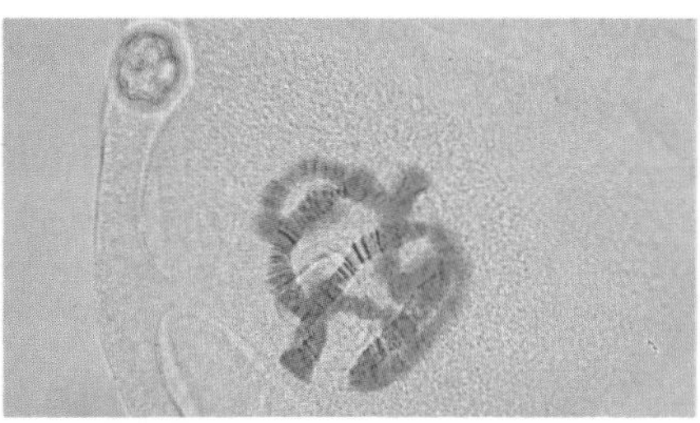
Chromosomes in the nucleus of a *Drosophila* (fruit fly) cell

Human cells have 23 matching pairs of chromosomes, making 46 in all. One of each pair is inherited from each parent. The chromosome sets shown have been made by cutting up photographs of two cell nuclei. The final two chromosomes are the sex chromosomes. They control the sex of the baby.

When sex cells are produced they carry only one chromosome of each pair. As a result each sex cell has one sex chromosome only.

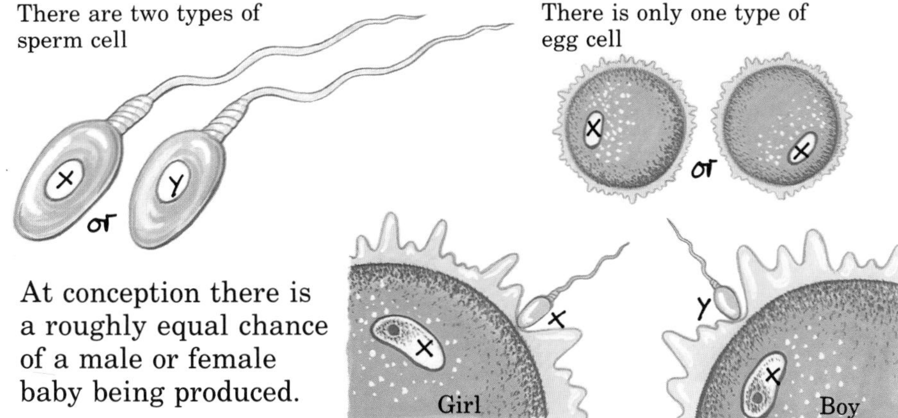

At conception there is a roughly equal chance of a male or female baby being produced.

The gene for colour-blindness is recessive and is on the X-chromosome.
Collect colour-blind test cards.
Test boys and girls for colour blindness. Keep a record of the results.

1 What are sex chromosomes?
2 Which sex chromosomes are carried by
- females
- males?

3 Use diagrams to explain why you would expect equal numbers of girls and boys to be born.
4 Why would you expect more boys than girls to be colour-blind?

Drug busters

Some people get involved with drugs. Usually they don't understand the dangers. Some of the dangers of two of the most common forms of drug abuse amongst teenagers are described below.

DRUG BUSTERS 1

Solvents are for suckers

Well, it can't harm you the first time

. . . can it?

And if it becomes a habit . . .

solvent abuse will damage your

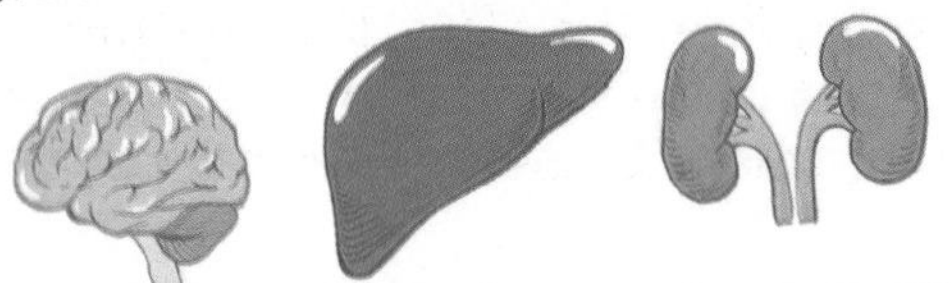

ALCOHOL ABUSE

The effect of alcohol depends on how much you drink and how often.

- Alcohol affects behaviour. It changes your emotional state and can make you aggressive or silly.
- It slows down your reactions and spoils your co-ordination and balance.
- Heavy drinking over a period of time leads to addiction.
  Drinking alcohol causes weight gain.
- Too much alcohol can cause liver and brain damage.

1 Write a description of the short-term and long-term effects of solvent abuse from the information above.

2 Produce a similar illustrated poster with the title *Drug Busters 2* to describe the dangers of alcohol abuse.
Cut out magazine pictures or make your own drawings.

Digestive enzymes

Enzymes are proteins that control chemical reactions in living things. Every enzyme works best around one particular temperature and over a small range of pH. Enzymes are important to digestion. All food types are finally digested in the small intestine but the digestion of carbohydrates begins in the mouth and the digestion of proteins begins in the stomach.

Different digestive enzymes act on different food types as the word equations below show.

amylase enzyme + starch (a carbohydrate) → maltose
protease enzyme + proteins → amino acids
lipase enzyme + fats → fatty acids + glycerol

Investigate the effect of pH on the activity of the enzyme amylase.

1 Compare the speed of the basic method (described below) with any other mixtures you decide to try.
2 After your experiments are complete predict what the pH of your saliva is. Test your prediction.

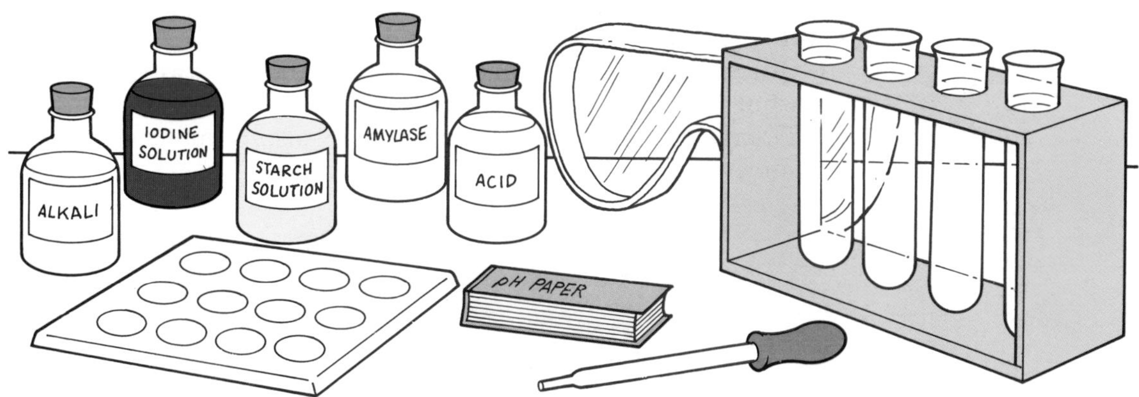

Basic method

- Mix the starch and amylase in a test tube. Find the pH of the mixture.
- Every two minutes transfer a drop of the mixture to one well in the dimple tile.
- Add a drop of iodine solution to this well. A black colour shows starch is still present.
- If there is no black colour the digestion of starch is complete.

1 Make a table to summarise the information at the top of this page. It should include;
   - food types
   - enzymes involved
   - products of digestion
   - where it happens.

2 Write a report on your experiment.

Stimulating time

We are aware of the environment around us because of our sense organs. Each sense organ or **receptor** is sensitive to a particular message or **stimulus**. If the stimulus changes we can make a **response** by changing our behaviour.

For example, the stimulus *light* is detected by receptors called *eyes*. If the light gets brighter we might respond by shading our eyes.

There is a pattern in this behaviour;

stimulus	→	*receptor*	→	*response*
bright light		eyes		shade eyes

The nervous system is the **co-ordinator** that links the receptor to the muscles or **effector**. This causes the response.

Now the pattern looks like this;

stimulus	→	*receptor*	→	*co-ordinator*	→	*effector*	→	*response*
light		eyes		brain		arm muscles		shade eyes

Collect an earthworm in a Petri dish.

1 Quickly (but gently) touch the tail of the earthworm. Watch what happens.

2 The two muscle sets that allow the worm to move are shown below.

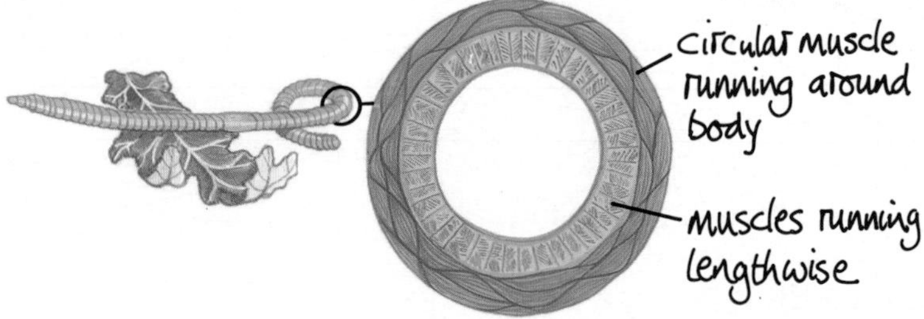

Repeat the experiment. Work out which muscle set contracts.

1 Make a list of the words in bold above.
Write down their meaning.

2 Describe the behaviour pattern for the following actions (in the same way as in the example above).
  a Covering your ears when a firework goes off.
  b Moving your hand from a hot surface.

3 Write a report on the earthworm experiment. Include drawings.
Describe the behaviour pattern in the same way as in question 2.

It's the way you say it

Human beings are social animals. We can communicate with one another by speaking and listening, and by reading and writing. Four forms of communication that use signs, sounds or signals are shown below.

A .–	B –...	C –.–.	D –..
E .	F ..–.	G ––.	H ....
I ..	J .–––	K –.–	L .–..
M ––	N –.	O –––	P .––.
Q ––.–	R .–.	S ...	T –
U ..–	V ...–	W .––	X –..–
Y –.––	Z ––..		
0 –––––	1 .––––	2 ..–––	3 ...––
4 ....–	5	6 –....	7 ––...
8 –––..	9 ––––.		

Morse code alphabet

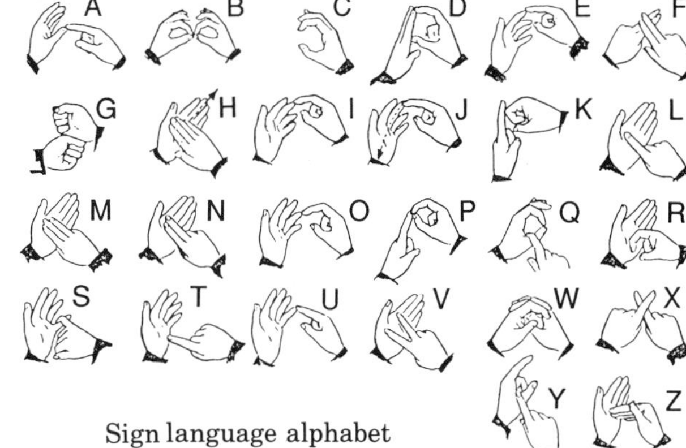

Sign language alphabet

Road signs/symbols

A B C D E F G H I J

K L M N O P Q R S T

U V W X Y Z and for of the

Braille alphabet

Collect

Pin
Coloured pencils

1 Write your name in Morse and in Braille (push the pin through the paper from the other side to make raised dots). Try it in sign language.
2 Communicate the name of your three favourite colours to a partner by
   - tapping out Morse for colour 1
   - signing the word for colour 2
   - writing colour 3 in Braille.

   Now discover the colours your partner likes best.
3 Design two signs without words that would communicate two of the ideas below. Use colour carefully.
   - electric car
   - danger, acid rain
   - hot surface
   - danger, noise pollution.

Poor eyesight

Many people have problems with their eyesight. They cannot focus on things clearly. The two most common eye defects are short sight and long sight.

Short sight

Long sight

The problem in both cases is that the eye lens cannot focus the light onto the retina. This may be because the eyeball is too long or too short, or because the lens does not work properly. The defect can easily be overcome by putting lenses in front of the eyes – either as contact lenses or as spectacles.

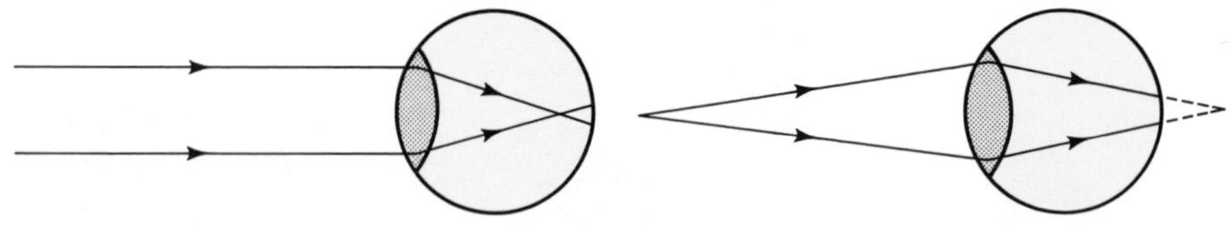

Short sight: eyeball too long or eye lens too strong

Long sight: eyeball too short or eye lens too weak

What sort of lens is needed to correct poor eyesight?

Collect

Poor eyesight sheets
Ray box
Lenses

1 For short sight:
   a Place a ray box lens at X.
   b Pass parallel beams of light into the lens (they will focus in front of the retina).
   c Put lenses at Y and try to make the focus move back onto the retina.
2 Repeat **a, b** and **c** with the long-sight diagram.

1 Report on the types of lenses needed to correct short and long sight.
2 Copy the pictures, which show the range of clear vision for three eyes. Label them *Normal, Short-sighted, Long-sighted.*

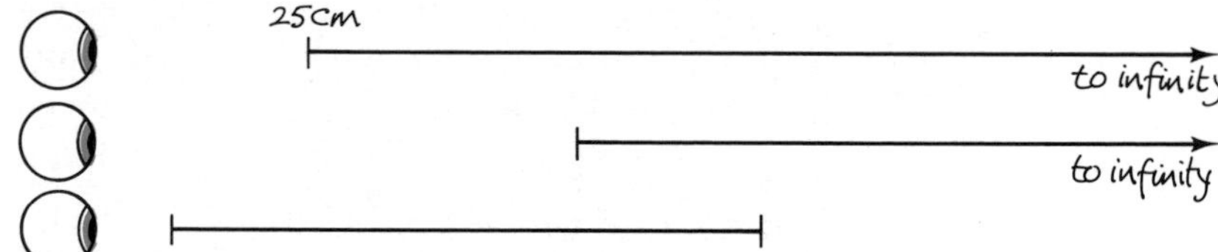

Electromagnetic waves

Light consists of waves which carry electric and magnetic energy through space to our eyes. These waves are called 'electromagnetic' waves, or **electromagnetic radiation**. The waves move forward at colossal speed - about 300 000 km/s.

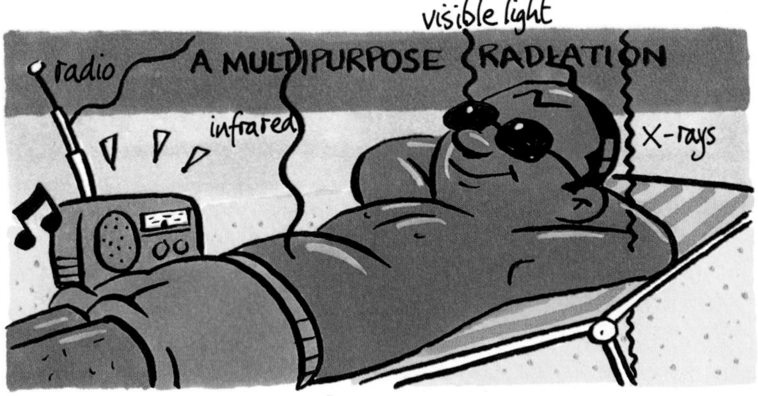

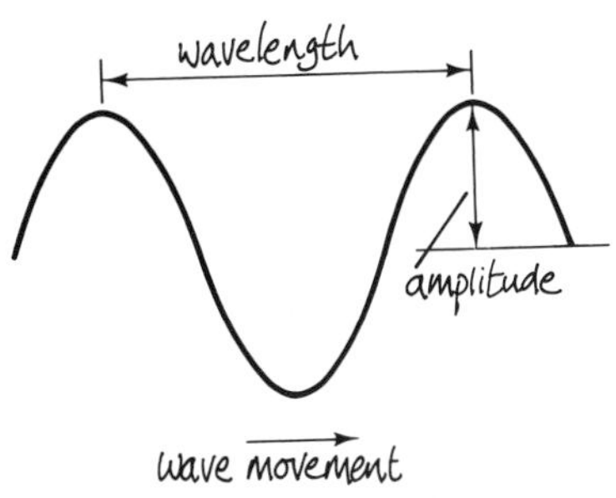

The Electromagnetic spectrum
There are different types of electromagnetic radiation, depending on the **wavelength** of the waves. Each type is produced and detected in its own way, and has a different effect on our bodies. The wavelengths vary over a wide range. The picture shows them spread out according to their wavelength into an electromagnetic 'family' or **spectrum**.

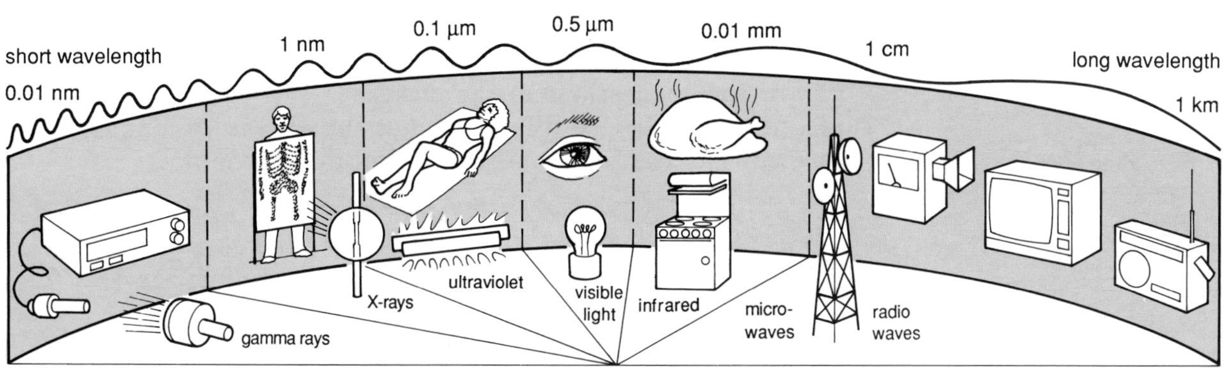

The electromagnetic spectrum

1 **Collect** the information sheet on electromagnetic waves.
2 Cut out the fact cards and stick them in your book in order of increasing wavelength. Use the picture to help you.

1 Which electromagnetic waves can we detect with our senses?
2 Describe one use that has been found for each type of radiation.
3 Which type of radiation can
a cause a suntan **b** toast bread **c** be used to take photographs
d be used for remote control?

Singing in the bath

People enjoy singing in the bathroom because the sound bounces off the walls, giving extra volume and richness to their voices. Sounds are greatly affected by the surroundings. Your singing would sound quite different in a cathedral compared to on a football pitch.

Many musical instruments also use echoes to improve their sound. They bounce their sound waves across air trapped in a box or cavity and produce complicated echoes. These add quality and interest to the sound.

If you clap your hands in a cathedral or a large hall, the sound may take several seconds to die away. The sound sets off in all directions and is reflected by the walls many times over, filling the space with multiple echoes. This is called **reverberation**. Cathedrals have stone walls that reflect sound well and the echoes take a long time to die away. Concert halls full of people do not reflect the sound so well and have shorter reverberation times. The walls must be carefully designed to give some echo or else the hall sounds 'dead' and heavy.

Reverberation can be added electronically to recorded sounds. Multiple 'reflections' of different strengths and durations are added to the original sound to give it 'atmosphere'. You can often hear this done to voice parts on pop records.

Collect

Tuning fork
Small box
Megaphone
Guitar
Scarf
Mug
Rubber band

The pictures show some ways to investigate reverberation.

1 Follow the suggestions in the pictures.
2 Listen closely to the difference that the air cavity makes, especially to the tone quality and volume of the note.

Write an article on *Reverberation*, including observations from some of your own experiments.

High–low–loud–soft

A skilful whistler can make low notes, high notes, soft notes and loud notes. These sounds can be made visible so that the differences between them can be seen.

Sound waves are pressure pulses in air and are invisible. A microphone can pick up the pressure pulses and turn them into an electrical signal. This cannot be seen either, but an oscilloscope can freeze and display the signal as a wave on a television-type screen.

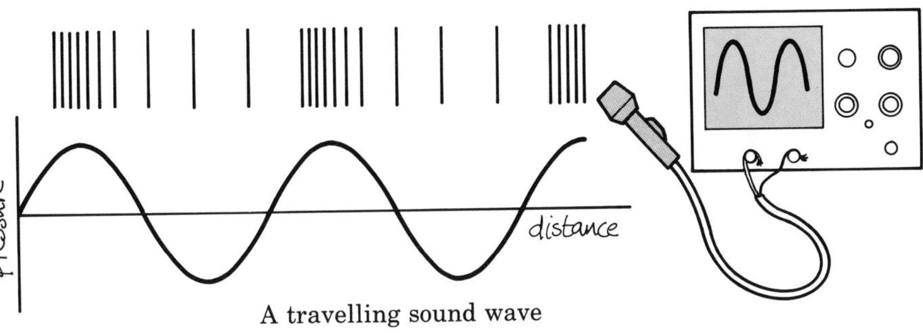

A travelling sound wave

Collect

Microphone
Oscilloscope

Whistle into a microphone and produce a simple sound wave.

1 Make high notes and low notes (you are changing the pitch of the note when you do this). Notice the difference that pitch makes to the sound wave.

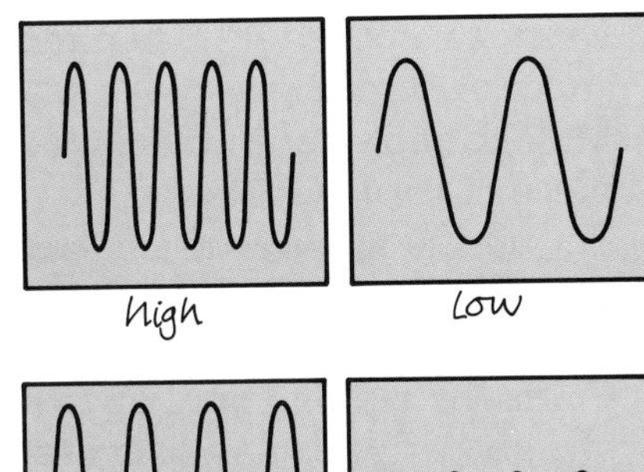

2 Make loud notes and soft notes (you are changing the loudness when you do this). Notice the difference that loudness makes to the sound wave.

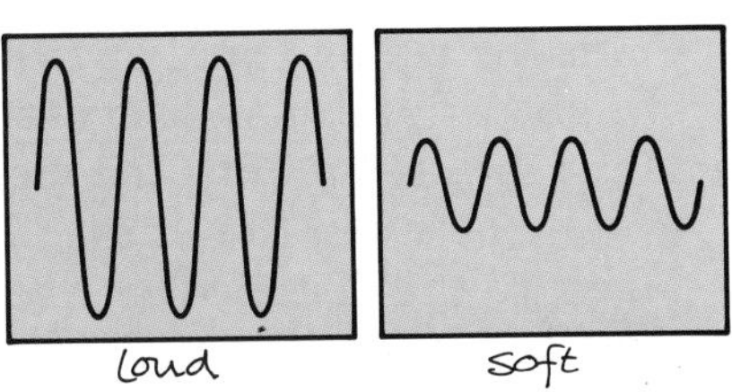

1 Copy and complete these sentences.
   a High notes have ______________ waves than low notes.
   b Loud notes have ______________ waves than soft notes.

2 Draw the wave picture you would expect to see of
   - a high soft note
   - a low soft note
   - a low loud note
   - a high loud note.

Sun sums

In earlier times the Earth was thought to be flat. In ancient Greece, Aristotle (384–322BC) first suggested that it was a sphere. He noticed that the position of the stars shifted as he travelled from north to south, and that during a lunar eclipse the Earth cast a curved shadow on the Moon. A fellow Greek, Eratosthenes (276–194BC), showed by an experiment that the Earth cannot be flat and at the same time estimated its circumference.

On a curved Earth the Sun may be directly overhead in Syene but not in Alexandria. In Syene the stick casts no shadow, but in Alexandria it does

He argued that if the Earth *were* flat and the Sun a long way off, identical vertical sticks would cast shadows of the same length anywhere in the world. He measured such shadows at midday on the same day of the year in two Egyptian cities 800 km apart. They had different lengths, so the Earth cannot be flat.

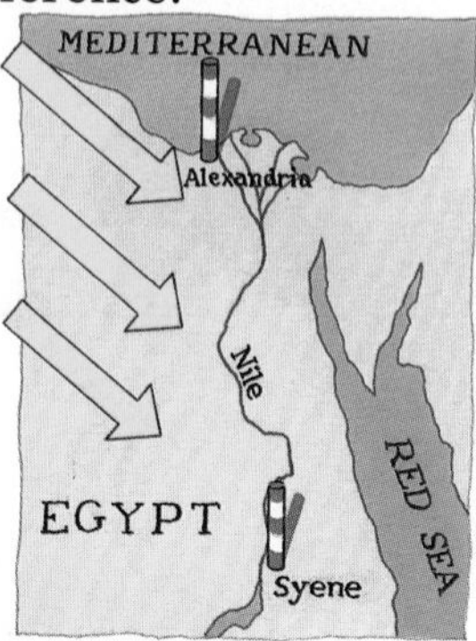

If the Earth were flat, the stick would cast the same length of shadow in Alexandria and Syene

From the difference he calculated the Earth's circumference to be about 40 000 km, not much more than the correct value.

The Sun is a sphere too. You can estimate its diameter from simple measurements.

Set up the apparatus shown in the diagram.

1 Draw two parallel lines 5 mm apart on a sheet of card.
2 Make a pinhole in the centre of the second piece of card.
3 Set up the apparatus as shown.

DO NOT LOOK DIRECTLY AT THE SUN.

4 Point the clamp stand at the Sun. A circle of light will fall onto the card on the base.
5 Move the clamp until the circle of light fits exactly between the lines.
6 Measure the distance between the 2 pieces of card.
7 Calculate the diameter of the Sun using this equation.

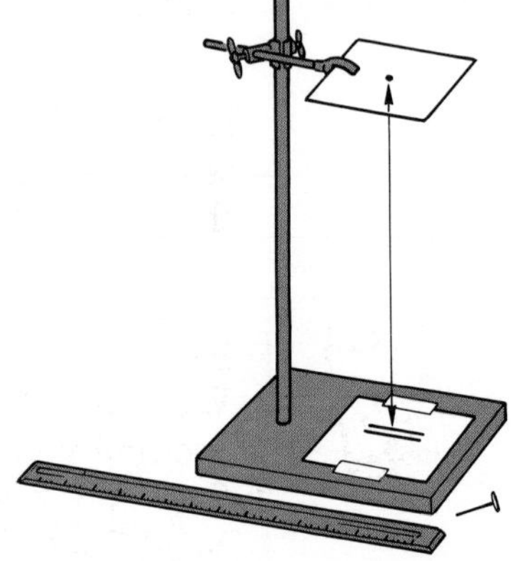

$$\text{diameter of Sun (km)} = \frac{\text{diameter of circle (5 mm)} \times \text{distance to Sun (150 000 000 km)}}{\text{distance between pieces of card in mm}}$$

1 Write a newspaper article describing ancient and modern evidence that proves the Earth is not flat.
2 Draw and label the apparatus for your experiment. Show your calculation for the Sun's diameter.

Winds of change

The photograph shows a satellite picture of a hurricane. The cloud pattern is typical of an area of very low pressure called a **depression**. Air rushes towards the centre of the depression from areas of higher pressure. This wind spirals into the centre or **eye** of the hurricane at over 100 km/h in the same way as water drains from a sink.

False-colour satellite photograph of a hurricane over the Gulf of Mexico

The differences in air pressure are caused by uneven heating of the air. The breezes you notice at the seaside on a hot day are caused by this uneven heating of the air over land and sea. Where the air is warmer the air pressure will be lower.

Collect

Tray of sand
Tray of water
Thermometer
Timer
Lamp

Design and carry out an investigation to find out whether water or sand

a heats up more quickly (lamp on)

b loses heat more quickly (lamp off).

Use the data you collect to predict which direction the sea-breeze should blow during the day and at night.

1 How are strong winds produced?
2 Write short reports on each experiment. Include your conclusion.
3 Copy the map of the Welsh coast opposite. Draw arrows on your map to show the direction of wind around this low. From which direction would the wind be coming if you lived in
   - Llanelli
   - Swansea
   - Carmarthen
   - Llandeilo?

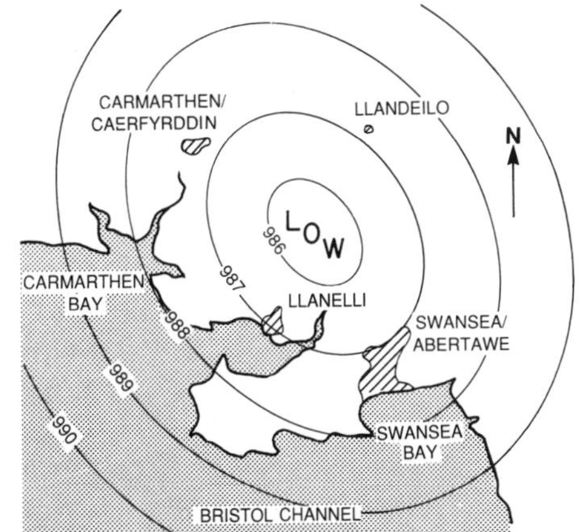

Earth features

Two hundred million years ago the Earth would have looked quite different from space. Geologists believe there was a single landmass that they have called Pangaea. They think that this land mass broke up and that the pieces moved apart to form the continents and oceans we recognise today. This happened because the Earth's crust is made up of many different pieces called **plates**. These plates continue to move very slowly, so 50 million years from now the continents and oceans will have different shapes.

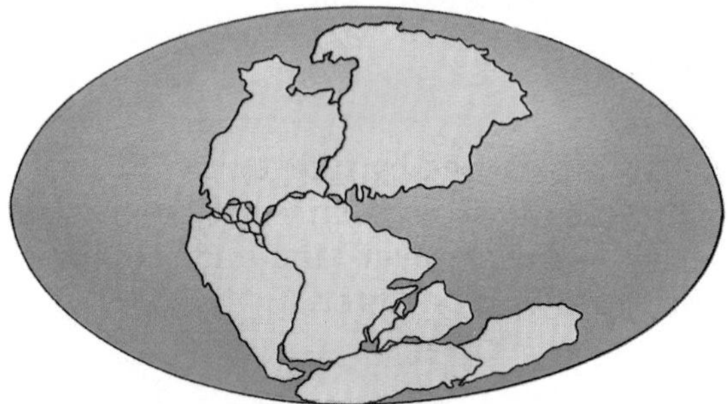

The Earth 200 million years ago

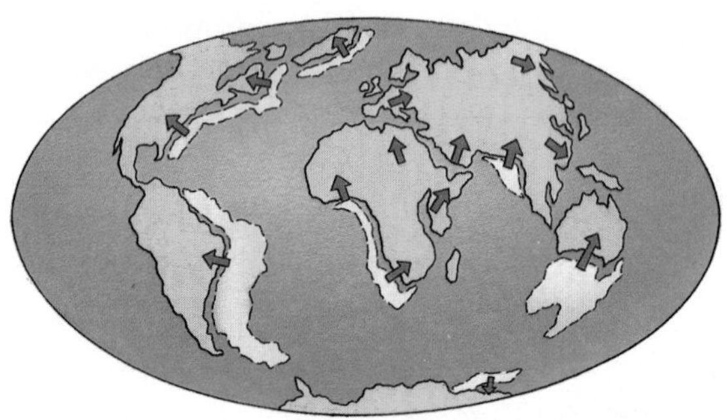

The Earth 50 million years from now

Weak points on the Earth's surface are found where two plates meet. These are zones of active crust where there is a danger of volcanic eruption or of earthquakes.

Far left: Mount St Helens in Washington State, USA, erupted in 1980

Left: the earthquake in California in 1989 caused a lot of damage

1 How do scientists think the present distribution of continents and oceans came about?
2 Why will the present position of the continents change?
3 Where are zones of active crust found? What can happen in these zones?
4 Find out about the Mount St Helens eruption. Write a short description of what happened.

You can't make energy (or destroy it)

Think about a wound-up spring that is accelerating a clockwork toy. The potential (strain) energy in the spring changes into kinetic energy and heat as the toy runs along. An important law of nature says that the total amount of kinetic energy and heat produced equals the energy lost by the spring.

If the spring loses 20 joules of potential energy then 20 joules of energy must appear in other forms – kinetic and heat in this case. There can be no overall loss in energy; nor can there be more at the end than you started with. Energy cannot be created or destroyed.

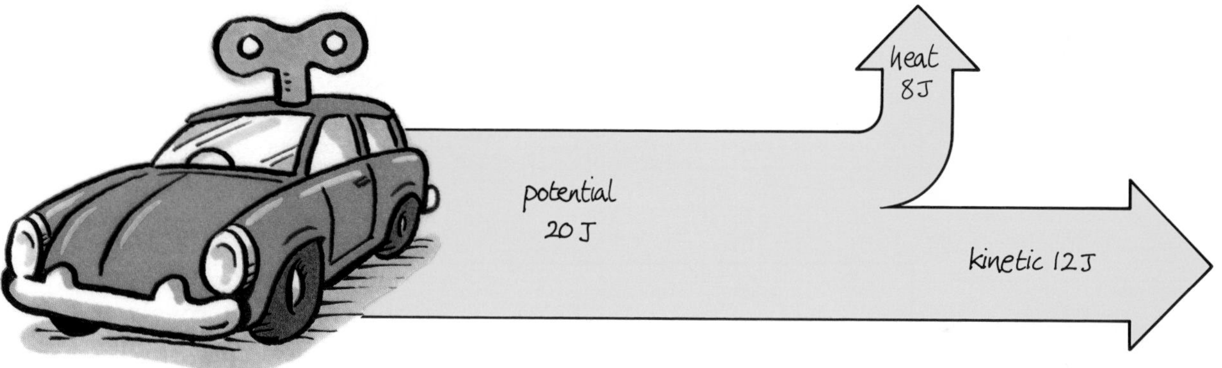

Although no energy is lost, the heat energy produced cannot be used again. It is 'waste' and of no further use. So when we use stored energy it eventually gets spread around as waste heat. This makes things slightly warmer but it is energy that cannot be extracted for further use.

Find out what it means to use 50 000 joules of energy:

- boil a kettle of water for 15 seconds
- dry your hair for 50 seconds
- run upstairs 10 times
- watch TV for 100 seconds
- listen to music for 1000 seconds.

Each of these activities uses about 50 000 joules of energy.

1 Find a way of displaying this information on a chart.
2 What eventually happens to the 50 000 joules of energy? Why is it not as useful once it has been used?

Cutting energy costs

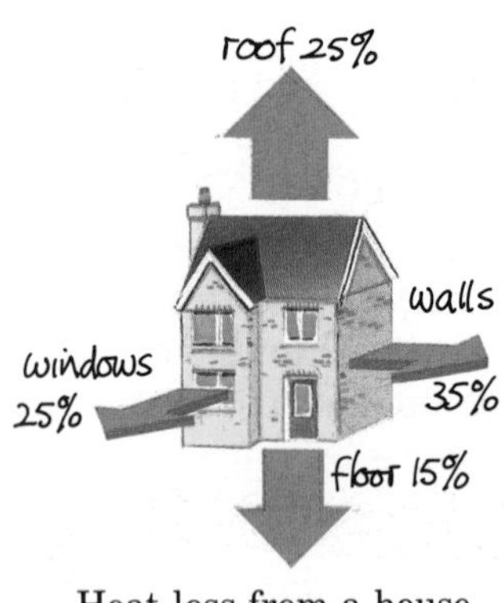

Heat loss from a house

The main way that a house loses heat is by conduction through the roof, floor, windows and walls. The pictures show how these losses add up.

Modern houses are built from materials that are designed to reduce these losses and so save us money.

The pictures also show examples of how heat losses through windows, roof and walls can be reduced.

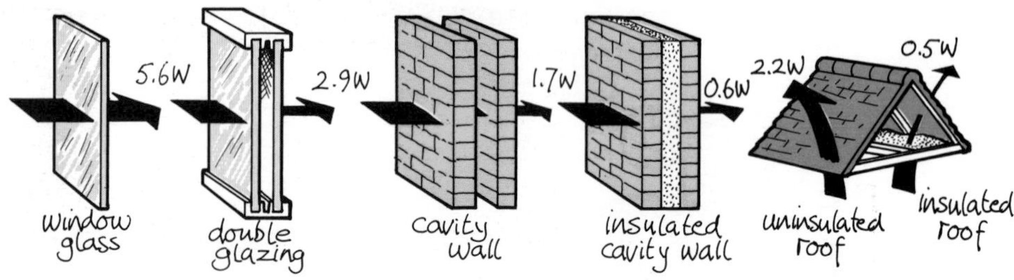

Ways of reducing heat loss

Collect

Iron
Drawing pin
Grease
Timer
Sheets of material (do **not** use plastics)

1 Design an experiment that tests how fast heat travels through materials. The picture gives you an idea of how to do it.

Work out the details giving

- step by step instructions of what to do
- what to measure
- which variables to control
- how to make it a 'fair test' for different materials.

2 Try out your experiment if you can and get some results.

1 Write down the instructions for doing your experiment.
2 Present your results in the form of a bar chart.

The cost of electricity

Electricity is often used to produce heat in our homes. We pay for electricity after it has been used. It passes through a meter that measures how much we use. The dials of the meter go round as the electricity is used and record the amount of energy that passes. The energy is measured in kilowatt-hours (also known as units). One kilowatt-hour is 3 600 000 joules. Modern meters show the reading directly in numbers. Older meters have dials with small pointers.

To read an older meter follow these two rules.

- Start with the largest dial and work downwards.
- If the pointer is between two numbers record the smaller one.

You should finish up with a 5- or 6-figure number.
Because the meters do not start from zero you have to take two readings, one at the start of the period you want to measure and the other at the end.

You usually have to pay for electricity four times a year. The bill looks like this.

METER READING		UNITS USED	UNIT PRICE (pence)	V.A.T. code	AMOUNT £
PRESENT	PREVIOUS				
67338	66264	1074	5.660	0	61.92
STANDING CHARGE				0	9.78

E = Estimated Reading. Please read the advice given on the back of this bill
C = Your own reading

YOUR REFERENCE NUMBER	YOU CAN PHONE US ON	NORMAL READING DATE	AMOUNT TO PAY
012.5306/147.018	01-730 6807	20 JUN 84	£71.70

From the bill, write down
a the two meter readings **b** the number of units used
c the cost of a unit **d** the cost of the electricity.

Find out how much electricity you use at home in exactly 24 hours.
How much would this cost if the price of 1 unit were 7p?

More speed

We like to go fast. It is thrilling, and journeys take less time. Most vehicles have a speedometer to measure speed.

Speed can also be measured from the time it takes to travel a known distance. It is calculated by dividing distance by time.

$$\text{average speed} = \frac{\text{distance}}{\text{time}}$$

The unit used in science is the metre/second (m/s or ms^{-1})

Collect

Tape-measure
Chalk
Timer
Clock

Speed-trap
Find out if the vehicles on a road near your school are breaking the speed limit. Take great care to stand well back from the kerb and follow your teacher's instructions. Do not go onto the road for any reason.

1. Make two marks 50 metres apart along the pavement.
2. Work out a way of timing cars over that distance.
3. Record the times and number plates of each vehicle.

1. Draw up a table that includes all your results and calculations. If possible use a computer spreadsheet to do this. Program it to do the calculations for you.
2. Write a letter to the Minister for the Environment about speed limits. Argue about the benefits and dangers of travelling at high speeds in towns and in the countryside. Say whether you want the law about speed limits to be changed.

Floating in air

It is possible to fill a balloon with natural gas so that it just floats in the air (ask your teacher for instructions).

When this happens, the forces on the balloon exactly balance out. The downward forces (the weight of rubber, thread and gas) are exactly balanced by the upward buoyancy of the air. If the upward and downward forces do not balance the balloon will slowly rise or sink.

Water also gives buoyancy to objects. Its buoyancy supports the weight of boats so that they can float. Even objects that do not float are supported by the buoyancy of the water so that they seem to weigh less.

Collect

Plasticine
Bowl of water
Balance
Weights

Design a boat made from Plasticine or clay that will support as much weight as possible.

Try to make a boat that can carry more than its own weight.

1 Describe the design of your most successful boat and give the greatest weight it was able to carry.
2 Most people can float in deep water without moving their arms or legs. If you can float describe how you do it.

Next time you go swimming try and float in the way shown in the picture – provided you can swim, that is!
The buoyancy of the water balances your weight and lets you feel something of what it is like to be 'weightless'.

An efficient weight-lifter

A small weight can lift a large one using this simple machine. The small weight falls and turns the wheel. This turns the axle that winds up the large weight.

The small weight puts energy into the machine as it falls. The large weight rises and gains energy from the machine.

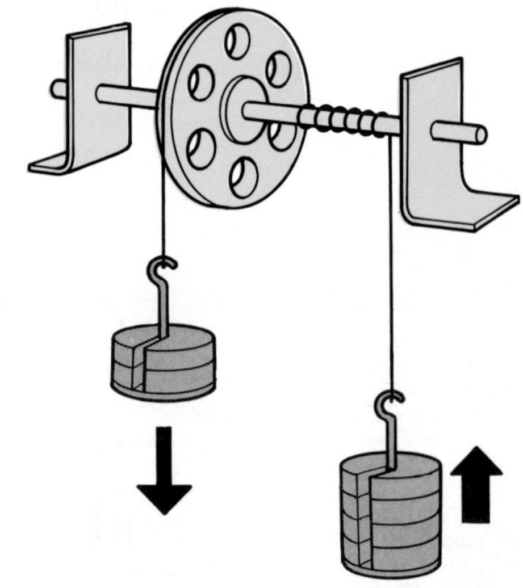

An efficient lifting machine

These energies can be calculated:

energy put in	E(in) (joules)	=	small weight (newtons)	×	drop (metres)
energy got out	E(out)	=	large weight	×	rise

E(out) is always less than E(in) because the machine itself uses some energy.

The ratio $\frac{E(\text{out})}{E(\text{in})}$ is called the **efficiency** of the machine.

Collect

Construction kit
2 mass hangers
Masses
String

Build a machine and measure its efficiency

1. Use the construction kit to build the machine.
2. Tie the weights on and adjust them until the small one can just lift the large one.
3. Measure the weights and the distances they move.
4. Calculate E(in), E(out) and the efficiency.

1. Write a report of your machine including a picture, your measurements and your calculations.
2. Draw the energy arrow for your machine to scale.

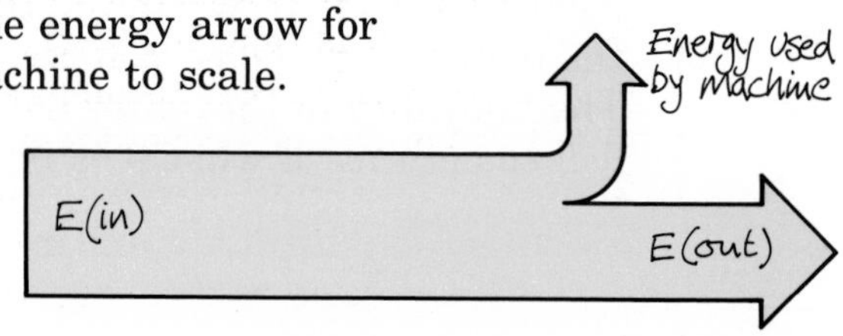

Energy used by machine
E(in)
E(out)

Activity plan

Collect the following equipment and substances.

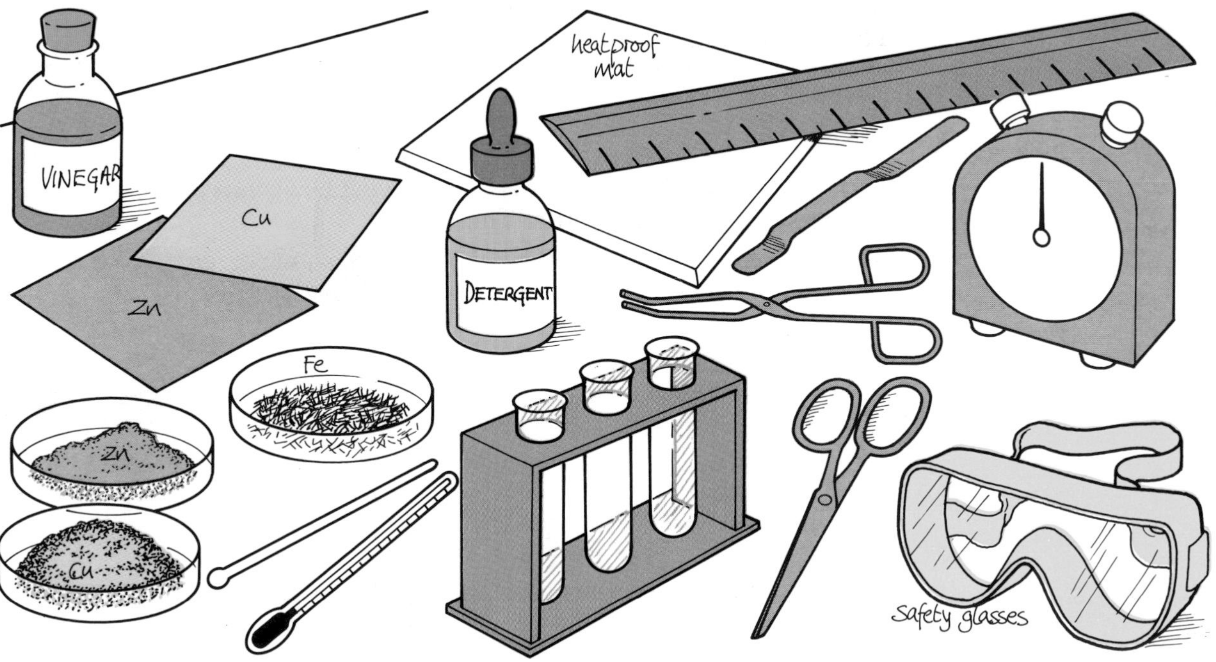

Some metals react with vinegar to produce hydrogen gas.
Your task is to plan and do an experiment to find out the order of reactivity of the metals with the vinegar.

1 **Plan** your investigation.
  a Look at the results of your experiment in 6.1A.
    Write down your hypothesis about the order of reactivity of the metals with the vinegar.
  b Discuss the following with your partner(s).
    At each stage **write down** your group decision.
    i Which *variable* will you change in your investigation?
    ii What other variables will you have to *control* to make a comparison fair? List these.
      How are you going to control each one?
    iii What can you observe and (if possible) *measure* about the reaction that will help you to decide how well each metal is reacting with the acid?
      It will be best to measure something if you can.
  c Let your teacher read your plan.
2 Follow your plan. Record your results.
3 Write a comment on your results.
  Did they agree or disagree with your original hypothesis?

Speedy reactions

Just as in cooking, other reactions can sometimes be speeded up by increasing the value of one or all of these variables:

- the temperature
- the amount of a reactant
- the number of pieces of a reactant (by decreasing their size).

1 Use these ideas to explain in a sentence why
  a powders that neutralise stomach acid work faster than tablets which do the same job
  b car exhaust pipes rust much faster than other parts of a car
  c sawdust and twigs burn faster than tree trunks
  d fruits ripen quickly during a hot summer
  e freezers keep food from 'going off' quickly
  f chips cook faster than boiled potatoes
  g whole carrots cook slower than diced carrots
  h pure oxygen is used in welding equipment to produce a very hot flame
  i a car engine needs more air when it is cold
  j most plants do not grow well in the winter
  k battery acid destroys clothes but acid in fruit does not.

2 Write down other examples of reactions which are affected by one of the three variables, *temperature, amount of reactant, size of pieces of reactant.*

Collect

Sodium hydrogen carbonate
Acid crystals
Anything else you need

If you have time, investigate whether the reaction that occurs in **cremola foam** is affected by the three variables. The reactants are an acid (*citric* or *tartaric*) and sodium hydrogen carbonate. Report your findings.

Redox reactions

Rusting of iron

Many foods decay if they are left in the air for long enough. For example, when the flesh of an apple turns brown, the oxygen in the air has reacted with the apple. A reaction in which the reactant gains oxygen is called **oxidation**. Other examples of oxidation are shown in the pictures.

When one substance gains oxygen, another must lose it. The loser in these cases is the air. A loss of oxygen is called **reduction**.

Burning of petrol

Oxidation and reduction are two halves of a reaction story. They can only occur together and the whole process is called **redox**. A good example of a redox process is the smelting of copper. Smelting could have been discovered by accident like this.

Respiration of food

The green copper ore is heated by the fire and forms black copper oxide. This mixes with the hot carbon ashes and a redox reaction occurs as described by the word equation

copper oxide + carbon → copper + carbon dioxide.

Tarnishing of silver

The copper oxide has been **reduced**. The carbon has been **oxidised**.

Green copper ore (malachite)
Charcoal (carbon)
Iron ore
Any equipment you need
Safety glasses

1 Design and carry out a laboratory experiment to find out if the reaction in the cartoon above is possible.
2 Find out if iron ore can be reduced by red-hot carbon.

Write a report about your investigations.

6.4 Extension

Using the reactivity series

Read the reactivity series of metals on page 96.

High temperatures are needed to make iron

Different metals were discovered at different periods in history. Silver and gold have been known since ancient times. They are so unreactive that they are found in the Earth as free elements, uncombined with others. On the other hand, more active metals like iron are always found combined with other elements. Such metals could only be separated from these compounds when people were able to make a furnace that produced a high temperature. The most active metals form compounds so well that electricity and heat are needed to get them out as free metals.

Gold was found long ago uncombined

Collect

Reactivity series data sheet
Components for the circuit
Zinc
Copper
Iron
Magnesium
Tin
Lead

1 Use the information above to predict the missing *dates of discovery* on your data sheet. Record your predictions and then check them with a data base or in the reference books available.

2 Set up this electrical cell.
  a Read the voltmeter and write down the voltage on your data sheet.
  b Swap the zinc for a piece of iron. Note the voltage on the sheet again.

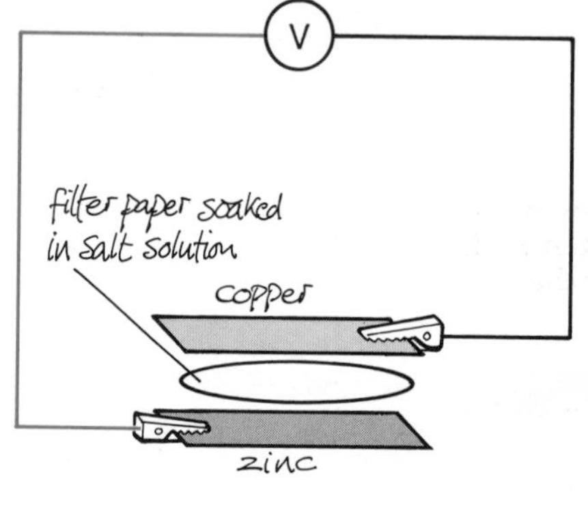

Refer to the reactivity series and predict the missing *voltage values* on the data sheet. Record your predictions, then check them by experiment.

1 Why is a pattern like the reactivity series useful?
2 Look at the reactivity series of metals and explain why
  a rings and bracelets are made from metals at the bottom rather than the top of the series
  b water pipes are made from copper rather than magnesium
  c ships containing a large amount of aluminium burn fiercely
  d hydrochloric acid can be safely used to clean copper but not to clean sodium.

Ionic compounds

There are two main types of compounds.

1 **Ionic** compounds are those which contain ions.
An ionic compound is usually made from a metal joined to a non-metal.
Collect and examine a model of an ionic lattice.

The **metal** ion is **positive**

The other ion is **negative**

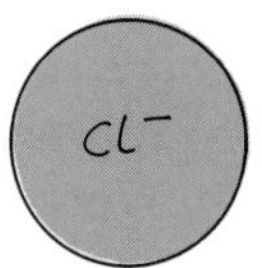

The ions have **opposite** charges: they are strongly **attracted**. They form a huge network called an **ionic lattice**. This network is very **strong**.

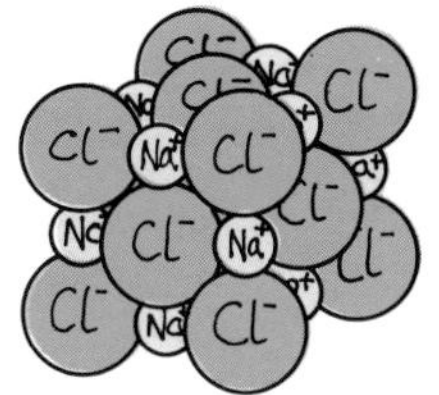

However the lattice is **broken down** by heat or water. The charged ions become **free** to move. The substance will now conduct electricity

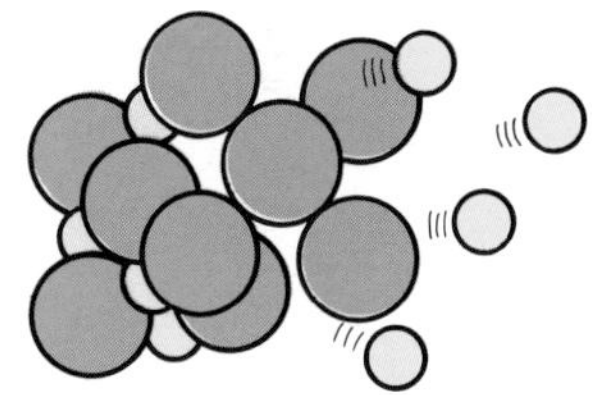

2 **Covalent** compounds do not contain ions.
A covalent compound is usually made from two or more non-metals joined together.
Collect and examine a model of a molecule.

Covalent compounds often contain small uncharged **molecules**

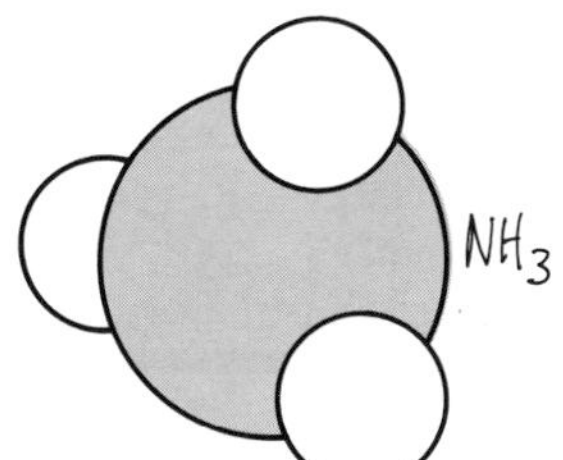

The molecules are not strongly attracted. They can be **separated easily** by **a little** heat and sometimes by water. However, without charged particles, the substance cannot conduct electricity

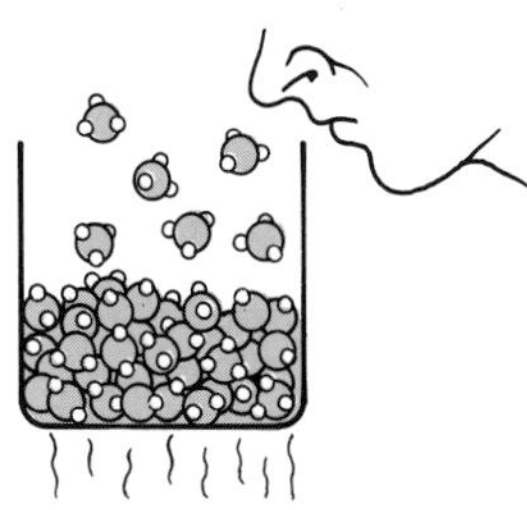

Collect

Set of solutions
Bulb or ammeter
Power supply (set at 4 V DC)
3 connecting wires
2 crocodile clips

1 Set up this circuit.
2 Use the circuit to discover which solutions contain ionic and which ones contain covalent compounds (if you do not know what to do then re-read the passage above). Record your results.
3 Collect a formulae card and check your results (refer to a periodic table to work out whether a compound is ionic or covalent).

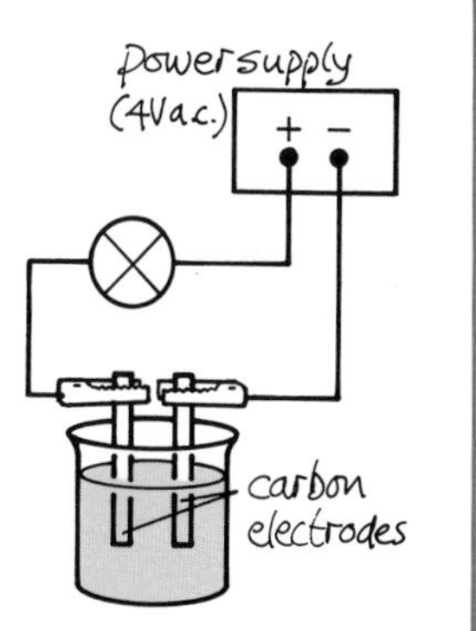

Write a short summary about the differences between the two types of compounds (you can look for more information in the books available).

Magnetic music

Music can be 'stored' on magnetic tape. Recording tape is made from strong thin plastic, coated with very fine magnetic powder.

The sound signal is converted into a current in an electromagnet, called the 'read/write head', made from a coil of fine wire wound on an iron core. The core is an almost-closed loop with a narrow gap where it touches the tape. When current passes through the coil it produces a strong magnetic field which magnetises the strip of tape that lies across the gap. In this way the waves of sound are converted into waves of current that produce a pattern of magnetic stripes on the moving tape. These faithfully store the music until it is wanted. The same head is then used to convert the magnetic stripes back into electric current and then into music.

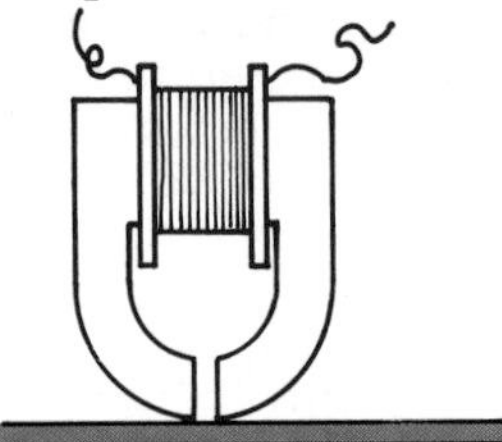

A magnetic tape head

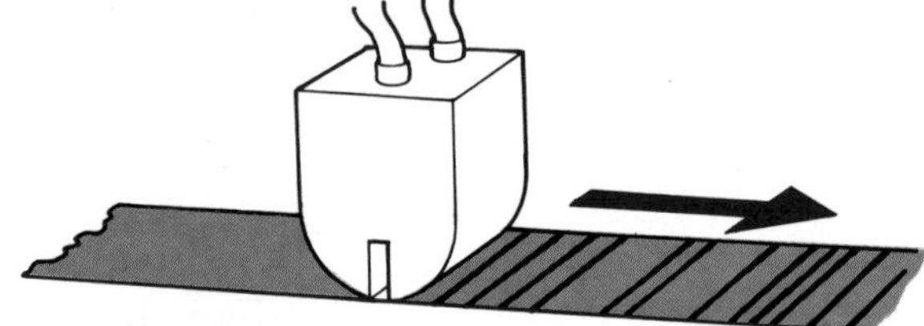

Magnetic tape head in action

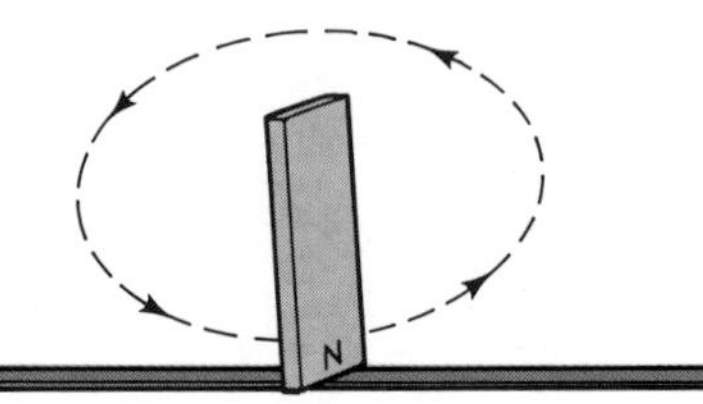

1 **a** Record this sentence on a tape recorder and play it back to make sure it is clear.
b Stroke the piece of tape that holds this recording with a magnet. This remagnetises the coating and wipes out the recording.
c Listen to the section you have remagnetised.

2 **a** Use a tape recorder and microphone to record some notes from a guitar, a keyboard, or other instrument.
b Check the quality of the recording by playing the recorded note and the instrument together.
c Investigate the recording of low and high notes in this way.

Collect

Tape recorder
Tape cassette
Magnet
Musical instrument

1 Explain whether it was easy or difficult to erase an audio tape using a magnet. Why should magnets be kept away from computer discs?
2 Write a report of your investigations into the quality of a tape recording.

Do-it-yourself electricity

You have seen that if you put electricity into a motor, it spins.

If you spin the motor, it makes electricity! The motor can be used as a **dynamo** to make electricity from other forms of energy.

Collect

Dynamo
Lamp
Gears
Weights
Thread

Use the equipment to build a machine that uses . . .
energy from a falling weight to . .
turn gears that . . .
spin a dynamo that . . .
makes an electric current that . .
lights a lamp.

(The gears are needed because the dynamo has to spin quickly.)

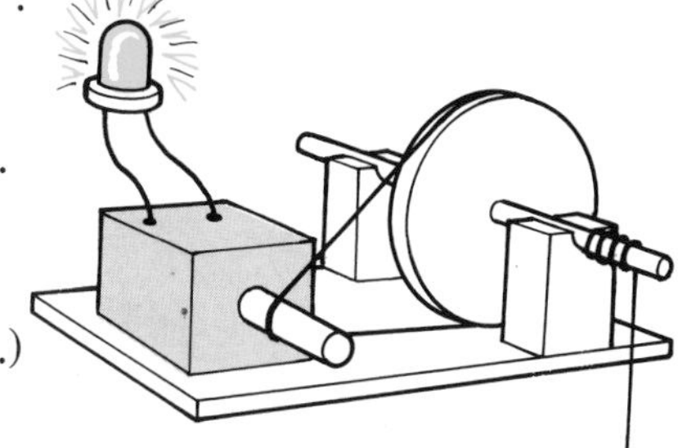

You have seen that if you put a changing electrical signal into a loudspeaker it makes sound waves.

If you put sound waves into a loudspeaker it makes a changing electrical signal. It is then acting as a **microphone**.

Collect

Loudspeaker
Oscilloscope
Connecting wires

Connect a loudspeaker to an oscilloscope and sing into it. Adjust the oscilloscope to show the changing voltage that your sound generates. Report on your findings.

1 The same machine can be used to make movement or make current. Copy this box and write *dynamo* and *motor* in the correct spaces.

current in		movement out
movement in		current out

2 The same device can act as a *loudspeaker* and a *microphone.* Copy this box and fill in the spaces with the correct words.

sound in		changing voltage out
changing voltage in		sound out

Secret messages by light pipe

It would not be difficult for a spy to 'tap' Nicola's message to Tariq (see p. 111) – unless they used a complex code that was difficult to crack. A safer way is to send the light message secretly along an optical fibre. This is a thin flexible thread of glass that can pipe light from one place to another. The light is put into one end of the fibre and travels through it until it reaches the other end. No light gets out even if the fibre twists and turns.

Many telephones are connected by optical fibres. When you phone a friend, your speech is coded into tiny flashes of laser light. These are sent along an optical fibre to an exchange near your friend, where the sound is put together again.

This happens at almost unimaginable speed. For example, if you sing a note for 1 second, you will send out about 250 sound waves. These are converted into 8000 short flashes of light that would take 1/10 000 second to travel 30 km along an optical fibre. This fibre could also be carrying 29 other conversations at the same time without them getting muddled up.

Collect

Press-switch
Optical fibre
Lamp
Battery
Box

Build your own optical-fibre secret communicator.
The picture shows a simple system you could make.

1 Write an illustrated report about your communicator. How secret is it?
2 Design and draw a small hand-held version of the transmitter.
3 Draw and label a block diagram of your communicator system.

Automatic experiments

Machines with memories can be used to collect data, such as readings from experiments. You could use a tape recorder, for example, to record your observations as you walk round a nature reserve.

Sometimes it is possible for the machine to do the experiment by itself and remember the readings for you to use later. This is especially useful if the experiment happens quickly or takes a very long time.

Here is an example of an automatic experiment you can fix up for yourself.

An automatic timer

Build a machine that measures the time it takes a steel ball to fall.

1 Make a top switch that starts the electronic clock when the ball begins to fall.
2 Make a bottom switch that stops the clock when the ball hits it (there is an instruction sheet available).
3 Line up your switches and let the machine time the ball for you.
4 Find the average time for 10 drops.

157	170	173	167	160	162	163	171
168	164	174	177	179	166	162	165
147	137	131	124	127	128	114	105
105	97	85	81	82	84	80	86
86	80	90	85	87	93	92	93
113	120	122	127	133	138	137	139
150	154	157	167	170	177	173	172
178	177	171	170	168	168	169	161
155	140	136	123	120	117	112	108
100	106	103	98	83	83	85	76
73	86	93	89	88	87	91	100
105	105	114	125	128	129	133	142
145	148	154	162	178	175	180	183
102	176	174	178	179	178	174	172
164	150	137	130	122	112	110	111
104	97	96	90	83	81	81	78
81	83	83	88	92	92	94	99
102	107	116	122	124	127	132	135
137	145	150	155	164	168	170	175
178	179	12	183	180	179	172	171
165	154	144	139	132	121	118	116
100	100	92	85	81	83	83	83
84	85	85	84	83	80	83	87
94	105	114	121	129	133	134	134
137	140	154	157	162	172	173	175
177	181	187	185	177	175	176	176
174	169	156	140	133	124	113	110
107	101	107	102	85	80	76	73
101	85	82	85	88	92	94	94
92	95	105	110	114	122	129	133
136	141	149	155	163	164	162	171
101	1185	0	0	0	0	0	0

A computer with a suitable sensor and 'interface' can do experiments, take readings and plot a graph of the results. The picture shows a computer set up to measure the shape of a sound wave from a pipe. The sound wave only took about 1/300th of a second to pass but in that time the computer took 256 separate readings of its size. It then plotted them on the screen to show the shape of the sound wave. This all happened automatically in a split second.
The computer also printed out the readings for you to work with.

1 Write a sales brochure for your automatic timing machine. Include a picture and describe all its good points.
2 Use some of the readings that the computer took, to plot a detailed graph of the sound wave. Read the figures in order, horizontally from left to right.

Electric charge on the move

The charging of an object with electricity can be explained by the movement of electrons. **Electrons** are small subatomic particles that carry a *negative* electric charge. When polythene is charged by rubbing it with a cloth, electrons move from the cloth to the polythene. This gives the polythene a negative charge (because it has gained electrons) and the cloth a positive charge (because it has lost electrons).

Collect

Van de Graaff machine
Thread
Ammeter
Connecting wire

In this experiment, electrons are forced to move down a thread.

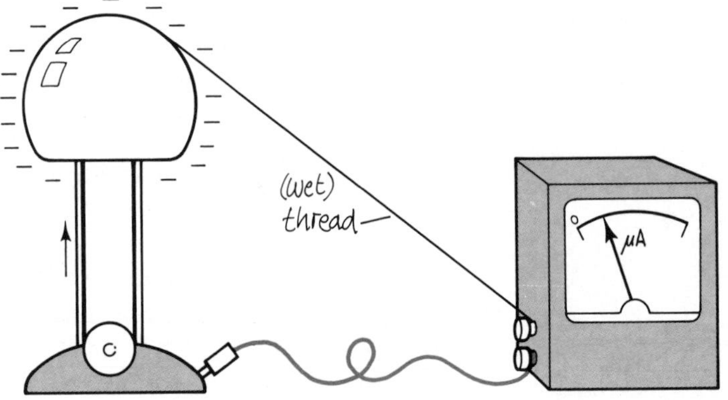

1 Connect a thread from the dome of a Van de Graaff machine to a very sensitive ammeter (ammeters measure electric current).
2 Complete the circuit with a wire from the ammeter to the base of the generator.
3 Turn the belt for a while and charge up the dome of the generator. Watch carefully what happens.

1 Describe carefully what happens to the ammeter from the moment you start to turn the belt until it stops again.
2 Do your observations fit in with the theory that an electric current is actually a flow of electrons?
Explain your answer carefully.

Using properties

There are thousands of materials in use today. Each one is suited to a special task. Your notebook may contain pages of paper held together with metal staples; imagine a book with metal pages and paper staples! Your home will be in a building made of bricks, concrete, metal or wood. Imagine a house made of food materials.

Real timber and brick house

Imaginary 'Gingerbread' house

1 Use a dictionary (or your own knowledge) to write a definition of these useful properties of materials: *heat insulator; soluble; dense; high melting point; waterproof.*

2 Look at the two house drawings.
Copy and complete the table to show one of the properties of the building materials used in each house.

	Real house	Imaginary house
Window	glass is insoluble	_____ is soluble
Walls	_____ is a good heat insulator	
Door	_____ is a dense solid	
Window frame	_____ is waterproof	
Chimney	_____ has a high melting point	

3 Explain why the material used for the roof of the real house is better than that used for the roof of the imaginary house.

4 The photographs below show materials that have been designed for a special use. In each case describe the properties that the material needs to have for this use.

a Epoxy carbon fibre for the Space Shuttle doors

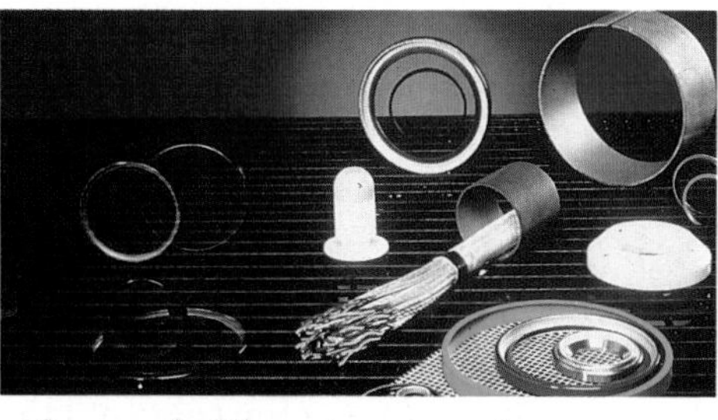

b Fluon to cover wires and seal engines

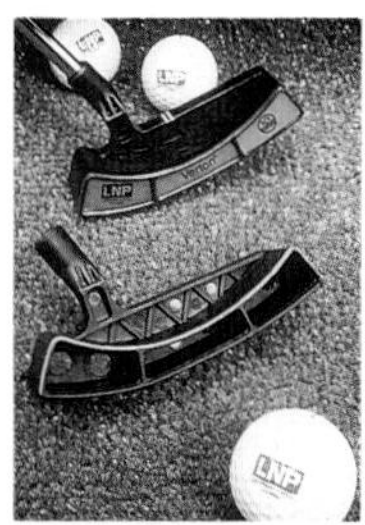

c Verton head for a golf putter

Suitable clothes

Consumer groups try to compare products scientifically to decide which are most suitable for the job that they claim to do. One group in Britain publishes a magazine called *Which?* containing reports about tools, TVs, washing machines and so on. Some of these describe how the materials that the product is made from were tested.

Collect

A consumer report
5 pieces of cloth
Anything else you need

1 Read one of the consumer reports available in the classroom. Pay particular attention to the tests that are described. Try to work out
   - what property was tested
   - what variable was measured
   - which other variables were controlled to make the test fair.

2 Design and carry out some consumer-type tests to find out which of the cloths would make the best suit of working clothes. The cloth will have to be long lasting to stand up to wear and tear.

   You will have to think about
   - how to test for wear and tear
   - what to measure
   - how to control the variables.

   You can collect the *Hints page* from your teacher **if you need to**.

Testing wear and tear

Write a report about your tests in the same style as the consumer report that you read earlier.

Thermal decomposition

Coal, petrol and wood are good fuels. All fuels burn to give out heat energy. Many other substances also burn when heated in air. They all give out energy whilst joining with the oxygen in the air to make new compounds called oxides. However, substances can also be changed by heat even when no air or oxygen is present. The manufacture of glass, concrete and brick uses heat at some point, yet these substances do not burn.

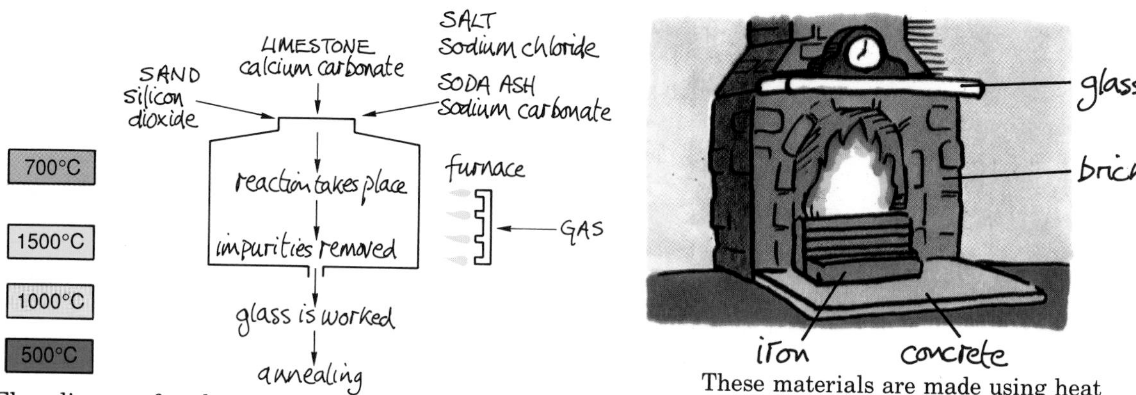

Flow diagram for glass manufacture

These materials are made using heat

Sometimes great heat can cause a substance to **decompose** (break up). The compound called ethene, used as a raw material for the manufacture of plastics, antifreeze and solvents, is made like this. Your teacher may show you how the process of *cracking* big molecules can produce little ones like ethene. The compound called calcium oxide (quicklime), used as a neutraliser to cancel out acids in the soil and in lakes, is also made by thermal decomposition.

calcium carbonate → *calcium oxide* + *carbon dioxide*
(limestone) (quicklime)

Collect

Any equipment that you need
Limestone
Limewater
Magnesium carbonate
Safety glasses

1 Select and set up equipment to show that limestone does decompose when heated to give carbon dioxide.
2 Magnesium carbonate is a compound found in rocks called dolomite and magnesite. Use the equipment to investigate whether magnesium carbonate will thermally decompose to produce magnesium oxide. (Magnesium oxide is very stable and is used to line furnaces.)

1 Give three examples of heat causing materials to
a burn **b** decompose without burning.
2 Write a report about your investigation. Try to make your thinking clear and include a word equation for any chemical reaction that occured.
3 Describe how heat is used to manufacture glass.

Alloys

The properties of a metal can be changed by melting and blending it with other metals. The new substance is called an **alloy**. Most modern metal objects are made from alloys rather than from pure metal elements. Steel alloys in a car are strong. Aluminium alloys in a ship are very light. Copper and nickel alloys in the coins in your pocket or purse are hard wearing and non poisonous. Some common alloys are

- stainless steel
  Fe+Cr+Ni
  (also contains C)
- solder
  Pb+Sn

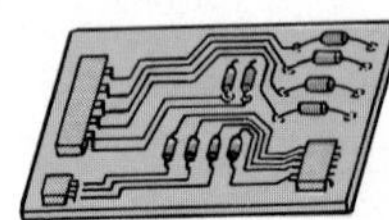

- bronze
  Cu+Sn

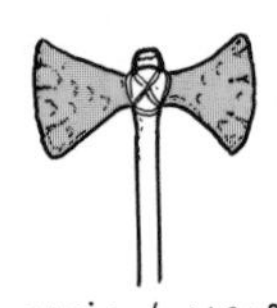

- duralumin.
  Al+Cu+Mg+Mn

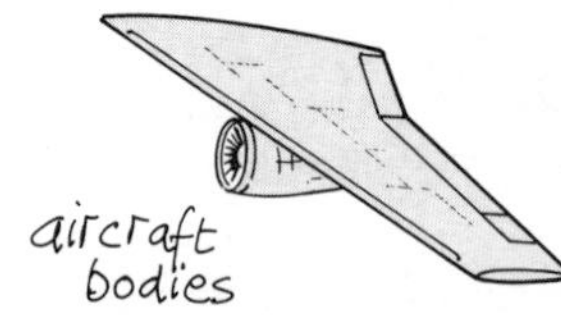

Collect

10 wires
Pliers
Solder
Soldering iron
Heatproof mat
Continuity tester
Safety glasses

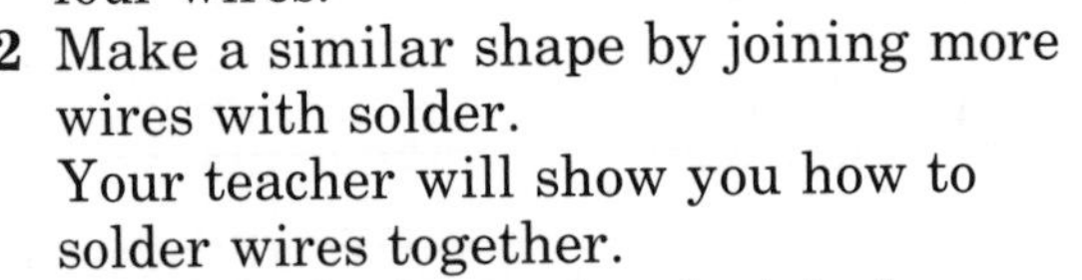

1 Make the shape of your initials like this by bending and joining three or four wires.
2 Make a similar shape by joining more wires with solder.
Your teacher will show you how to solder wires together.
3 Check both shapes for electrical continuity.

1 What is an *alloy*?
2 Make a table to show
 a the names of four common alloys, **b** the full names of the metal elements in each alloy, and **c** a use for each alloy.
3 What advantages has the use of the alloy
 a bronze over copper
 b brass over copper
 c stainless steel over iron
 d titanium alloy over iron?
4 Write a report about your soldering work, making clear what properties of the alloy solder were useful to you.

Material solutions

Many salts (and other materials) are soluble. They dissolve in water to form a solution. Dissolved material is sometimes a source of water pollution. Living things can be harmed and even killed by dissolved substances. Some sources of river pollution are illustrated below. The numbers give the number of trout that were killed in one British river system over a period of 12 months.

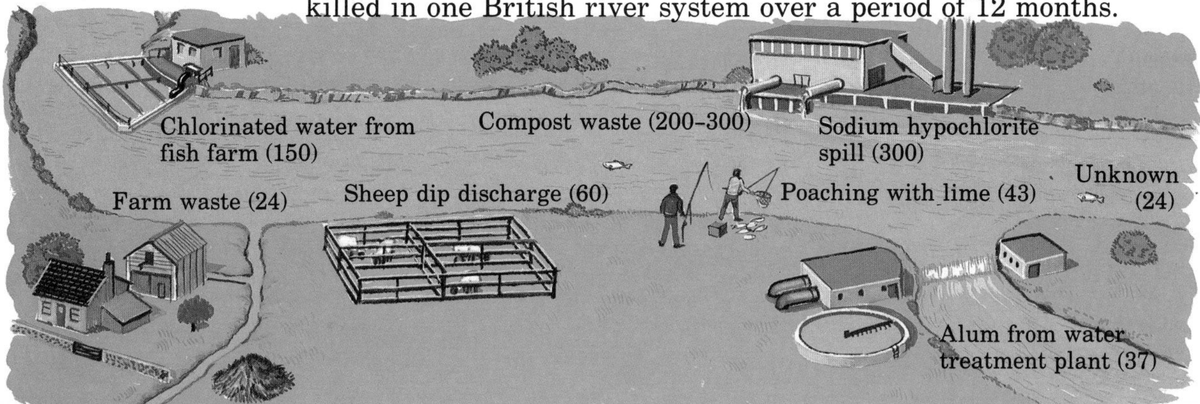

Collect

20 cm^3 pipette
Evaporating basin
Watch glass
Bunsen burner and heatproof mat
Desiccator
2 samples of water
Safety glasses

Fortunately the amount and type of dissolved material in a water sample can be measured. Follow the instructions below as accurately as possible and measure the amount of dissolved material in each of the two samples of water.

For each sample:

1 Heat the evaporating basin gently.

2 Cool the basin in a desiccator. Weigh it on an electronic balance. Record the weight.

3 Use the pipette to measure *exactly* 20 cm^3 of the water sample.

4 Put this water into the evaporating basin.

5 Evaporate the water. Reduce the heat when there is little water left so that there is no spurting of solids.

6 Cool the basin in a desiccator. Reweigh it. Record the weight.

1 Calculate the weight of dissolved solid in 20 cm^3 of each water sample.
2 Write a report about your analysis.

Index